HENS TO KEEP, EGGS TO EAT

Starting with Hens in the Garden

By

CHARLOTTE POPESCU

Published by Cavalier Paperbacks 2014

Cavalier Paperbacks

Burnham House,

Upavon,

Wilts SN9 6DU

www.cavalierpaperbacks.co.uk

ISBN 978-1-899470-33-4

Printed and bound in Great Britain by Jellyfish Print Solutions, Hollythorns House, New Road, Swanmore, Hants SO32 2NW

CONTENTS

INTRODUCTION

This book is designed to give you all the information you need to start off with hens in the garden. I want to concentrate on what you need to know before you buy your hens and the information you will want to seek out once you have them. Hybrids are one of the best options for families who keep a few hens in the garden so I have included details on the different sorts available and given you a comparison between the benefits of hybrids and pure breeds.

There are no legal restrictions on keeping a small flock of hens in your garden but do check with your neighbours to make sure they don't mind, especially if you are thinking of keeping a cockerel! Local authorities can take action if they get complaints about noisy cockerels or an increase in the rat population due to feed being left on the ground.

You only need to register in England with the Department for Environment, Food and Rural Affairs (DEFRA) if you have more than 50 chickens.

You do need to do some research before getting your hens and make sure you have the time to look after them. Hens are very rewarding but you do need to be around at the right time of day to let them out in the morning and shut them up at night if you don't want them at risk of predators. Obviously in the winter this could mean that you need to be shutting them up at 4pm and letting them out around 8am. They will put themselves to bed at dusk if not a bit before (unlike ducks who can see in the dark and so are not good at putting themselves to bed). You will need to check that they are all fit and healthy and collect their eggs every day, cleaning them out at least once a week.

WHY YOU SHOULD KEEP HENS

1. We may love our cats, dogs, pet rabbits etc but how about a pet that actually produces something edible in return.

2. You will save money by not having to buy eggs. You can sell surplus eggs and buy your hens' feed with your egg money, making them self supporting.

3. The eggs couldn't be fresher and all the family will enjoy collecting them.

4. Hens (and cockerels) have great personalities and will add beauty and interest to your garden, parading around with their different shapes, sizes and colours.

5. If you decide to keep a few hens you will be reducing the demand for shop-bought battery eggs and hopefully this will lead to less need for hens to be kept in cages.

6. Hens will eat your garden pests such as slugs, snails, earwigs, grubs, beetles and add fertilizer directly to your lawn.

7. Your hens will eat weeds such as dandelion, chickweed and dock leaves.

8. You can use the chicken manure as an activator in your compost bin.

9. Hens are very low maintenance – they do not need to be walked, brushed or kept inside.

10. It is a very satisfying hobby to produce your own fresh eggs and is an extension to growing your own vegetables – also you can feed surplus vegetables to your hens.

11. Your hens will endlessly amuse you and make a great talking point at dinner parties.

12. Keeping hens and maybe hatching some chicks later on will be an education for your children.

A SHORT HISTORY OF THE HEN

Today's hen originated from the Red Jungle Fowl, Gallus Bankiva, which came from a wide area north of India stretching down through Burma and Malaya to Java. This bird can still be found living wild in the remote jungles of Burma and Java. The Red Jungle Fowl was originally a small bird that escaped its predator by flying up into the trees. It had long wings and a long tail. This bird would lay about 30 eggs a year in two clutches, one in the spring and one in late summer (this gives you an idea of how far the domestic fowl has progressed in its egg laying capacities!). When man started the domestication process these birds were developed for cock-fighting, an important sport for ancient civilizations and a favourite pastime of the Romans and the Greeks.

The first references to domestic fowl in literature occur in a Chinese encyclopaedia compiled in 1400BC. Chickens appear on Babylonian carvings dated at around 600BC. Later, around 400BC there are references in Plato in which he complains about people preferring cock-fighting to labouring.

It is thought that fowl were introduced to Britain possibly by Phoenician sailors who had chickens transported to North Africa from India and brought them on to the Mediterranean coastal countries and then to Britain. Certainly the Romans found poultry already in Britain when they arrived in 54BC. Julius Caesar refers to the Britons as keeping fowl for amusement but not for eating, so we may assume cockfighting was already prevalent.

The chicken breed that has remained the closest to the Red Jungle Fowl is the Old English Game which is very similar in appearance and was the breed developed over the centuries for cockfighting. Cockfighting became very popular in Britain between 1750 and 1849. Feeding and training the cocks was just as skilled a job as breeding them. They had to have their combs and wattles cut, their feathers and wings trimmed and their natural spurs were cut short so that artificial spurs or heels could be fitted. These could be anything up to 7cm in length but two cocks fighting each other had to have spurs of equal length. They inflicted cleaner wounds than the natural spurs. Cocks also used their beaks and wings in the fights. A fight would carry on until one cock was killed or refused to continue fighting. In 1849 an Act was passed to make cockfighting illegal in Britain but it is still practised in Spain, the Far East and some of the Latin-American countries.

It is thought that the Romans may have introduced a breed that is now known as the Dorking to Southern England when they settled here. The Dorking, characterised by its five toes, was described by Pliny and Columella in the first century. Possibly certain types of chicken were bred in different parts of the country but on the whole birds were still mainly bred for cockfighting.

Bantam is the name of a town and district in the north west of Java. In 1595 the Dutch established themselves at Bantam and in 1602 the English occupied Java. The locals sold the beautiful jungle fowl from Bantam to the British who took them back to England. Eventually the word Bantam was used to describe all small poultry. Many breeds nowadays are available as large fowl or as miniatures which are commonly known as bantams but, technically, a true bantam does not have a large fowl counterpart.

Marco Polo on his journeys in the early 1300s described seeing chickens with 'fur' and must have been referring to the Silkie Breed, but it wasn't really until the 1800s that poultry, having been developed around the world, were imported into different countries and it was then that breeds of poultry began to be established in Britain. It is believed that Christopher Columbus brought the first chickens to America on his second trip there in 1493.

During the last 150 years the idea of keeping chickens for pleasure and not just for profit or sport came into fashion with the start of Poultry Shows. Many smallholders were in existence before the First World War and between the Wars many ex-servicemen set up poultry farms which were totally free-range. It was after the Second World War that more intensive systems began to be used such as the deep litter system, where hens were housed indoors on straw. Then in the Sixties and Seventies intensive battery-cage systems were used extensively with hens spending their entire laying lives in small cages. Commercial egg production became big business and still is but at least more and more of us are keeping hens in our gardens now. From 2012, EU law made the battery cage illegal, although 'enriched' cages are still allowed. These cages are bigger with small perches and a nest box area.

THE BREEDS

There are over 200 breeds of chickens recognised worldwide and when you take into account all the colour variations in each breed there are a lot of varieties to choose from. Pure Breeds are divided into 'heavy' and 'light' breeds, 'soft' and 'hard' feathered – and the majority of them are available as large fowl or bantams; some of the pure breeds are true bantams and only available as such. Then there are the hybrids which have been developed in recent years to be specifically good at egg-laying.

PURE BREEDS

The Different Types

We really need these pure breeds, both heavy and light, as without them there would be no hybrids!

Heavy Breeds - Soft-feathered

The Heavy breeds are generally the brown egg layers and have red earlobes. The large fowl are big, weighty birds. Heavy breeds are historically those developed for utility production also known as dual purpose (good for meat or for eggs), many of them having a good reputation for egg laying. The majority of heavy breeds have an excellent temperament, which makes them suitable for a variety of purposes and ideal for beginners or children. Examples of heavy breeds are Barnevelder, Brahma, Orpington, Marans, Plymouth Rock, Rhode Island

Red, Sussex and Wyandotte – most of these are also called sitters which means they will go broody and want to sit on some eggs in the spring.

Light Breeds – Soft-feathered

Many of the light breeds are of Mediterranean origin. These are the white egg layers, most having white earlobes. Examples are Ancona, Andalusian, Appenzeller, Leghorn, Minorca and Poland. They tend to be more nervous and excitable as they are much more lightweight than the heavy breeds and are not used for meat. The two exceptions to the rule of white eggs are the Welsummer and the Araucana. The Welsummer, although a light breed is not particularly lightweight, lays brown eggs and has red earlobes; the Araucana lays a turquoise egg and earlobes are concealed by thick ear muffling. Light breeds tend not to go broody and so are termed non-sitters. The Araucana though is an exception.

Game Breeds – Hard-feathered

The hard-feathered breeds are the 'game' breeds and on the whole not suitable for the garden. These breeds were used for cockfighting in the past. They include Asils, Indian Game, Modern Game, Ko-Shamos, Malays and Tuzo bantams. One breed, the Old English Game and can be kept successfully in the garden but they are quite flighty. Hens are small, laying predictably small eggs.

Here is a list of some of the most popular breeds for the garden (arranged alphabetically). Most are available as large fowl or bantams and all are soft-feathered.

APPENZELLER Light Breed White Egg Layer

Strictly speaking the Appenzeller is called Appenzeller Spitzhauben and was named after the local lace bonnets worn by the ladies of Appenzellerland in Switzerland. Spitzhauben actually means pointed bonnet and the crest on an Appenzeller also points forward, looking like a bonnet. These birds were imported into Britain relatively recently and have proved popular. They were classed as rare but recently The Appenzeller Society has been formed and they have been taken off the rare breeds list. Appenzellers can be silver- or gold-spangled, a rarer chamois-spangled or black. They are particularly attractive and very striking. The cockerels look magnificent with their beautiful tail feathers and small head crests. Birds can be quite nervous and hard to catch, being good fliers. There is no standardised bantam version.

ARAUCANA Light Breed Blue Egg Layer

Araucanas were bred by Indians from the Arauca Province of Northern Chile and they refused to let the Spanish conquerors crossbreed their hens thus preserving the breed. They are the only hens in the world to lay turquoise eggs (colours vary between green, olive and blue). Araucanas have crests on their heads and have faces covered with thick muffling. They come in many colours including lavender, blue, silver, pyle, black and white and there are large fowl as well as bantam versions.

There is also a Rumpless variation of the breed which, as the name suggests, does not have a tail but is favoured because it lays a large egg in relation to its body size.

See also Cream Legbar on page 46 and Skyline hybrid on page 43.

BARNEVELDER Heavy Breed Dark Brown Egg Layer

The Barnevelder is a Dutch breed which originated in the town of Barneveld in Holland. Most country people in the surrounding area of Barneveld were keeping poultry as early as the 12th Century. Around 1850 the poultry there were crossed with imported birds such as Cochins, Malays, Brahmas and Langshans. Egg production improved substantially and brown eggs were the preferred colour. The eventual result at the turn of the 20th century was the Barnevelder. The inhabitants of Barneveld always claimed that their chickens laid 313 eggs – being a religious community with no work being done on Sundays that meant 365 days minus 52 Sundays. However this was a little optimistic – egg production is more likely to be about 200 eggs a year. Barnevelders, as might be expected, are the most popular dual-purpose breed in Holland. The climate there is often cold, windy and damp which made Barnevelders a thrifty and hardy breed and very suitable for the similar climate in Britain. Barnevelders were imported into Britain in the early 20th century. The hens nowadays are good layers of dark brown eggs – Maranses were used to improve the dark brown colour of the eggs. Colour variations in the birds are black, double-laced (black with beetle green sheen), partridge and silver. A bantam version is available. Back in Holland Barnevelder hens have certainly helped the development of their native town, Barneveld, where poultry, eggs and associated products are still a major source of income in the area. The Dutch Poultry Museum is based there and it is also the home of the International Barneveld College, an educational poultry institute.

BRAHMA Heavy Breed Light Brown Egg Layer

The Brahma sometimes claimed to be a very old breed supposedly originating in India and early pictures show that it was very similar to the Cochin from China. The name Brahma is taken from the river Brahmaputra in India. However, it is now generally agreed that the Brahma was created in America from Shanghais or Cochins imported from China in the 19th century and crossed with Grey Chittagongs (Malay type birds from India). A crate of nine Brahmas was sent to Queen Victoria in 1852 from the American breeder, George Burnham, and thus the breed was introduced to Britain. Brahmas have distinctive feathered legs and feet, small pea combs and rounded plump bodies giving a compact appearance. They come in a variety of types and colours including buff Columbian (buff coloured with black in the neck and tail feathers), gold (black pencilling on a gold background), dark (black pencilling on a white background), light (black neck striping and tail feathers on a white background) and white. Brahmas can be very large (weighing in at between 5 and 6 kg) – they have a sort of majestic massiveness and have been variously described as 'noble and commanding', 'intelligent looking', 'with a neck well proportioned and finely curved as in a spirited horse'. They do need space but, because they don't fly, are easy to keep in a run. They have been used in the creation of many new breeds and in developing new colours in existing ones. Brahma bantams are available; they were developed by Mr Entwisle of Wakefield, Yorkshire in the 1880s. They are a good size for a bantam so ideal for smaller gardens and for children to pick up. Their partially feather-covered feet make it difficult for them to scratch so your garden should remain pretty much intact.

COCHIN Heavy Breed Light Brown Egg Layer

The Cochin originally came from China in the 1850s where it was known as the Shanghai. Cochins brought on boats from the port of Canton in Southern China were presented to the young Queen Victoria. They were first exhibited at the Birmingham Show in 1850 – Lewis Wright (*Illustrated Book of Poultry*) writes: 'Every visitor went home to tell of these new wonderful fowl, which were as big as ostriches, and roared like lions, while as gentle as lambs; which could be kept anywhere, even in a garret …' Originally with clean legs the Cochin became very popular owing to its size and laying powers. However exhibition breeders turned the Cochin into a 'bag of feathers' and it eventually lost its good name as a useful egg layer. Now similar to the Brahma with feathered legs and feet, it has a serrated single comb. There are no miniatures of this bird but Pekin bantams are a similar small version.

LEGHORN Light Breed White Egg Layer

The Leghorn is a very popular breed which originated from the Port of Leghorn (now Livorno) in Italy and was imported into Britain in the late 19th century, with first the white and then the brown birds. Leghorns have had the longest life of any of the productive breeds ever introduced. There is evidence from old pictures that this type of bird with a distinctive flop-over comb in the female was to be found in many countries of Europe. Old breeds such as the Belgian Brakel, Pheasant Fowls and the Scots Grey had similar features such as white earlobes, flop-over combs and laid white eggs. It is possible therefore that this Mediterranean type was the original fowl of Europe and that the heavier type of Leghorn evident today was due to crossing Malays, Cochins and Minorcas. Prolific layers, Leghorns do not go broody. There are now other colour variations available such as the increasingly popular exchequer, black, barred, buff, cuckoo, mottled and partridge, and bantams are miniatures of their large fowl counterparts. The white Leghorns are the best layers closely followed by the black ones.

MARANS Heavy Breed Dark Brown Egg Layer

English ships sailing into Marans near La Rochelle in France, in the 19th century used to carry hens and fighting cocks. These were exchanged for fresh hens from Marans and the region became the birthplace of a particular breed of poultry, originally called the Marandaise, later to become the Marans. Around 1880 two brothers, poultry merchants from London, were responsible for spreading knowledge of the Marans hens. One of them was a wholesaler of white Russian eggs (Russia was at this time an important poultry producing country). The other brother, whose ships docked at Marans, had the idea of competing with the white Russian egg trade by selling the dark brown eggs of Marans hens which were bigger and fresher. Thus the eggs soon became popular in the London markets. Maranses were crossed with Brahmas and Croad Langshans in order to make the eggs browner – Brahmas were used for their egg laying abilities and the Langshans for the dark brown colour of their eggs; other breeds used in the make-up included Faverolles and barred Rock. Maranses weren't actually introduced to Britain until 1929 – there are two types – French Marans and English Marans. The English are cuckoo (dark, golden or silver) or black and clean legged. These are recognised by British Standards. Also available here are the French varieties (not recognised by British Standards) which can be wheaten, splash, copper black, copper blue which are all increasingly popular and there is a rarer white and Columbian (white with black neck lacing) version; all these have feathered legs.

The French Ministry of Agriculture state that no salmonella bacteria are found in the eggs of Maranses, the reason being that the pores are smaller than other eggs and the outer membrane tends to be very thick. Maranses have single combs. The Marans is the one pure breed where it is relatively easy to distinguish male and female chicks – males have a white spot on the top of their heads while females have a darker one. They are a good choice of breed for free range as they are good foragers. The Marans' eggs are so special that in France competitions are held on the size, shape, texture and dark colour of the eggs. The colour ranges from brown to a dark chocolate colour. Bantams are a good size and will lay a good sized egg.

NEW HAMPSHIRE RED Heavy Breed Brown Egg Layer

The New Hampshire Red originates from 1915 in the US where it was bred from the Rhode Island Reds in New Hampshire, although the birds today are very different in colouring and body shape from the original Rhode Island Red. These birds were originally bred for the eggs. The body of a New Hampshire Red is well rounded with a deep full breast and medium length tail. The head is deep and rather flat on top with prominent eyes, a single comb with five points, smooth face, large wattles and oval red earlobes. The legs are yellow and the feathers are a deep chestnut red. The chicks are quick to feather up and mature. The hens lay well, are placid and friendly and therefore easy to tame. They thrive in a run or wandering free and as they are not good fliers, they do not need particularly high fencing. They do not have a tendency towards broodiness, although it does occur occasionally, and are good layers of brown eggs.

ORPINGTON Heavy Breed Light Brown Egg Layer

Orpington fowl were named after a village in Kent where William Cook first bred them in the late 19th century. The village of Orpington boasts a pub called The Buff with a sign displaying a Buff Orpington cockerel. Langshans, Minorcas and Plymouth Rocks were involved in its creation and today they still look similar to the Langshan. The black variety was followed by the white and then the buff. There are now other colour varieties such as blue, cuckoo, silver-laced, gold-laced and blue partridge types which are proving popular. The late Queen Mother used to keep large fowl Buff Orpingtons. The Black Orpington was re-introduced to Britain from Australia in the 1920s and called the Australorp. A later introduction was the Jubilee Orpington, which is rarely seen but has recently been added to the breeds listed by the Domestic Fowl Trust. Orpingtons are large, heavy and rather broad with short legs and an abundance of feathers which makes them look even bigger. They make good mothers and can sit on a large number of eggs. They do not fly because of their weight and also have relatively small wings in comparison to their size so are easily kept within the garden; they are docile and so good for first time poultry keepers with small children. They lay well and their eggs are light brown – they don't usually start laying until about 28 weeks and the eggs are smaller than you would expect when you look at the size of the hens. Bantams are also available in this breed and are very popular as they are docile and good with children.

PLYMOUTH ROCK Heavy Breed Light Brown Egg Layer

The well known variety is the barred Plymouth Rock (the 'barred' refers to the markings) but this breed is also popular in white and buff. It was developed in New England in the early 19th century from crosses of Dominiques, Black Javas and Cochins and first exhibited in 1869; they are still popular in the US. The Plymouth Rock was named by its founder DJC Bennett in honour of America's founding pilgrims who disembarked from The Mayflower, at Plymouth Rock (Massachusetts) in 1620. The Plymouth Rock is an excellent layer of tinted eggs. It is used in the development of the autosexing breeds (see page 45) as well as hybrids such as the Black Rock. Plymouth Rocks have single combs and yellow legs.

RHODE ISLAND RED Heavy Breed Brown Egg Layer

The Rhode Island Red is probably our best known breed. For most of the 20th Century it was the Rhode Island Red along with first crosses (i.e. with Sussex) that made up about 50% of Britain's laying hens. Nearly all of today's brown egg-laying hybrids have parents of different breeds but have the Rhode Island Red on at least one side of their ancestry. The breed originated in America on the farms of the Rhode Island Province. In 1854 William Tripp obtained a big Malay cockerel that had arrived from a south east Asian port. He ran it with his hens and found the resulting progeny was laying bigger eggs. John Macomber who lived in Massachusetts became interested and the two men worked together crossbreeding with Cochin China hens. The offspring was then crossed with light Brahmas, Plymouth Rocks and Brown Leghorns. The breed has been one of the most popular in Britain for all purposes especially in the past when people kept hens for meat as well as for eggs. The breed was imported to Britain around 1900 with the British Rhode Island Red Club being established in 1909. The Rhode Island Red hens and cockerels are a deep chestnut colour with yellow skin and legs. Although a heavy breed, on the whole they don't seem to go broody. A bantam version is also available but is quite hard to source.

SILKIE Light Breed Cream Egg Layer

The Silkie originated in Asia, some believe in India, others think in China or Japan. The breed may have been discovered by Marco Polo in the early 14th century near the south Chinese town of Quelinsu – he documented 'exotic oriental chickens that have hair like a cat, are black and lay the best of eggs'. Aldrovandi who wrote a treatise on chickens published early in the 17th century, describes Silkies as white as snow with wool like sheep. Their fluffy look led to the bizarre rumour that they were produced by crossing a rabbit and chicken and thus were sometimes referred to as rabbit-fowl. Silkies are famous for their broodiness and are covered in fine, silky fluff rather than feathers. The wings are also covered in this fluff which prevents Silkies from flying. Crested with a mulberry comb and wattles and turquoise earlobes, they have feathered legs and five toes. They also have a unique feature in that their skin and flesh is dark purple with almost black bones. Colours range from blue, gold and black to white and partridge. Silkies although small, are classified as large fowl but a small bantam version has been created which is docile and therefore popular with children. Silkies are well known for making fantastic surrogate mothers. Unlike other breeds they will take on other chicks, even ducklings. In times gone by, before incubators existed, Silkies were used as natural incubators by breeders not only of chickens, but also of pheasant, partridge and duck. Silkies do not cope well with wet, muddy conditions

– the silky fluff does not keep out the rain as other hens' feathers do. The breed is delicate and not particularly hardy; Silkies do not mix that well with other breeds.

SUSSEX Heavy Breed Light Brown Egg Layer

This is an old breed derived from the Old Sussex fowls which were bred in Victorian times for their meat and eggs. The oldest variety is the Speckled Sussex. The Light Sussex was developed in the county of Sussex using Brahmas, Cochins and Dorkings. Old English Game were used in the make up of the Browns and Buffs and were developed during the 1920s. During the second world war Light Sussexes along with Rhode Island Reds were popular breeds to keep for the dual purpose of eggs and meat. Colours can be from brown, red, speckled, silver and white Sussexes but light and buff are probably the most common colours. Sussexes have single combs and light coloured legs. The Sussex is a calm, friendly breed, so easily tamed. The hens are really good layers of light brown eggs and tend to lay in the winter as well. Sussexes may go broody and will make good mothers. Bantam versions are popular.

VORWERK Light Breed White Egg Layer

The Vorwerk was developed in Germany in 1900 by Oskar Vorwerk and is classed as a rare breed. Vorwerks make excellent hens for the garden because they are medium sized, attractive and thrive very well on less food than other breeds of the same size. Vorwerks are buff coloured with 'black belted' markings, which means the neck and tail feathers are black. They have distinctive white earlobes, single combs and grey legs. They are alert, very active and excellent foragers. They lay white eggs and go broody fairly easily. Vorwerks are good flyers so do not usually like to be confined. Vorwerks can be quite hard to source, but well worth seeking out if you want something a bit different.

WELSUMMER Light Breed Dark Brown Egg Layer

Although Welsummers are traditionally associated with Welsum in Holland the breed was originally created in the area along the river Ysel, just north of Deventer. The breed was developed in the early 1900s. In the early development of the breed Barnevelders, another Dutch breed, were used as well as Partridge Cochins, Leghorns and Wyandottes. At first these birds were called Welsumers but when they arrived in Britain around 1928 and a Breed Club was set up the name changed to Welsummer. Being a light breed you would expect Welsummers to lay white eggs and have white earlobes. In fact they lay dark brown eggs and have red earlobes. The colour of the eggs will vary slightly depending on the strain. Eggs have a matt shell rather than the glossy shell of the Marans. Welsummers were originally all a Red Partridge colour The cockerels always have reddish brown mottling on their black breasts but there is now a silver duckwing variety and a rarer golden duckwing. The silver duckwing hens have silvery white necks and salmon-red breasts; the cockerels are stunning with white neck and saddle feathers and black breasts and tails with a beetle green sheen. Welsummers have single combs and yellow legs. They are very active foragers so do well as free rangers. They don't lay as many eggs a year as some other breeds, but will go on laying in the spring/summer season into their dotage. Welsummers are classed as non-sitters but are known to go broody, depending on the strain.

WYANDOTTE Heavy Breed Light Brown Egg Layer

Originally known as the 'American Seabright' or 'Seabright Cochin', the exact origin of the Wyandotte remains unknown to this day. Some say the Wyandotte was named after a tribe of American Indians - the logo for the Silver Wyandotte Club of America contains a drawing of an Indian tepee. Some say that Houdlette, one of the first Wyandotte breeders named them after his father's ship, the Wyandotte. The silver-laced Wyandotte was the first Wyandotte variety accepted to the breed standard in 1883 in the US. Experts believe that the original Wyandottes were bred by crossing Dark Brahmas with Spangled Hamburghs and possibly Poland. Later in the breeds' history, other varieties were developed elsewhere in the United States. The Wyandotte was introduced into Britain in the late 18th century and by the early 19th century was very popular, along with the Leghorn, as an egg-laying breed. There are several different varieties nowadays which include gold, buff and blue-laced, partridge, Columbian (white with black neck lacing) and silver-pencilled. The Wyandotte has a rose comb and yellow legs. The large fowl tend to be very big and heavy looking so the bantams tend to be a good size are a popular choice for the garden because they look so attractive, particularly the laced and pencilled varieties. The bantams lay eggs which are almost as big as those of the large fowl.

SOME BANTAMS FOR SMALL GARDENS

The following breeds are all known as True Bantams as they have no large fowl counterparts.

BELGIAN BEARDED BANTAMS

Three varieties are standardised in Britain: Barbu D'Uccle (Bearded Uccle) is, as the name suggests, heavily feathered around the neck with feathered feet. It has a single comb and comes in many colour variations including black-mottled, lavender, porcelaine, quail, cuckoo, millefleur and blue. The amazing choice of colours in these bantams is probably unrivalled in any other breed. Barbu D'Anvers (Bearded Antwerp) differs from the Barbu d'Uccle in that it has unfeathered legs, a rose comb and in the males the wings are carried very low, almost vertically. Barbu De Watermael (Bearded Watermael) is crested and clean-legged, small and perky. All three remind one of a human wearing an overcoat with the collar turned up. These are some of the oldest true bantam breeds. A Dutch painting from the 17th century by Albert Cuyp reveals a small hen with similar markings to a quail-coloured Barbu D'Anvers. Belgian bearded bantam hens lay small cream eggs.

DUTCH BANTAM

These are some of the smallest bantams around but they are friendly and available in many different colours. The original bantams were only available as partridge coloured. Dutch bantams didn't arrive in Britain from Holland until the early

1970s and a Club wasn't formed until 1982. Dutch bantams are upright, active birds with a good covering of feathers. Wings are carried low but the tail is carried high. Hens lay a good number of small light brown eggs and make good broodies. Dutch bantams don't mind being confined but they are good fliers; they enjoy foraging and, being small, have small appetites.

PEKIN

The Pekin was introduced to Britain from China. In 1860 the summer palace of the Chinese Emperor at Pekin was sacked by English and French forces and some Pekin Bantams were brought home to England as plunder. The Pekin was originally thought to be a miniature of the Cochin, but in reality has no connection with it. Pekins are a genuine bantam breed and are small with feathered feet and are a wonderful tame breed for children. They are popular as they look round and cuddly. They come in a variety of colours including black, blue, buff, white, cuckoo, lavender and partridge. They don't lay particularly well and the eggs are small, being light beige. The hens go broody frequently and can be very persistent about remaining broody. Their disadvantage is that the feathered feet tend to get wet and muddy very easily. However the advantage is they won't scratch up your garden as they are hindered by their feathered feet. They will need dry conditions for perching so that their leg feathers can dry. The advantage of keeping Pekin cockerels is that they crow quite softly.

SABLEPOOT/DUTCH BOOTED BANTAM

The Booted Bantam or Sablepoot, as it is called in Holland and increasingly now in Britain, is an ancient breed. It was crossed with the Belgian Barbu d'Anvers to create the Barbu D'Uccle. The Booted Bantam has no muffling (beard and whiskers on the face) but does have feathered feet. These bantams can be black, white, millefleur or porcelaine in colour and lay small light brown eggs.

SEBRIGHT

Sebrights are true bantams and one of the oldest British varieties. The breed was developed by Sir John Sebright in the early 19th century. They are very small and slender, carrying their wings low and with prominent tails; hens and cockerels have similar plumage and rose combs. They can be gold or silver in colour; hens lay small white eggs.

SERAMA

This is the world's smallest bantam and a relatively new breed. It was developed in the Malaysian state of Kelantan, apparently from crossing Japanese bantams and some local Malaysian bantams. The birds are tiny and must weigh less than 450g to meet the Breed Standard. The breed is thought to be named after the Thai King Sri Rama who ruled in the 17th century, because of its proud upright carriage. The cockerel in particular carries himself very erect, with an upright tail, short body and protruding breast. Hens, not surprisingly, lay very small eggs. A breed club has been set up and officially recognised by the

Poultry Club in 2008. It is best to keep Seramas enclosed as they are particularly at risk from predators such as sparrow hawks and buzzards who will easily swoop down and snatch them.

MORE BREEDS

Breeds that are more difficult to source but could work well in your garden include: Australorps, Croad Langshans, Ixworths, Sumatras, Sulmtalers, Thuringians, Jersey Giants, Transylvanian Naked Necks and Dorkings, which are available as bantams as well as large fowl.

Breeds that are really quite hard to come across are Ancona, Dominique, Minorca, Andalusian, Scots Dumpy, Norfolk Grey, Scots Grey, Sultan, Hamburgh, North Holland Blue, Sicilian Buttercup and Marsh Daisy. Then there are birds such as Frizzles, Houdans, Orloffs and Yokohamas that are rare and kept mainly by people wishing to exhibit their birds.

Pure breeds not recommended for beginners are Fayoumi, Friesian, Campine and Lakenvelder - these are all light breeds which can be very flighty and nervous. They are all quite hard to source.

Here's a bit more information on these rare breeds:

ANCONA Light Breed White Egg Layer

The Ancona hen, as the name suggests, originated in Ancona, Italy. Both the cockerel and hen are similar in colour – a mottled black and white. The single comb on the female tends to flop over on one side. The hens lay white eggs and are very similar to Leghorns.

ANDALUSIAN Light Breed White Egg Layer

This breed owes its name to the province of Andalusia in Spain and is one of the oldest Mediterranean breeds. The Andalusian is blue, probably developed from crossing black and white birds. The female has a distinctive comb which flops to one side of its head.

AUSTRALORP Heavy Breed Brown Egg Layer

The Australorp was developed from the Black Orpington in Australia. The name originated from The Austral Orpington Club which was set up in the 1920s. The idea was to create a good egg layer but also to retain the meat quality of the Orpington. Australorps remain black with a brilliant green sheen and there is also a blue variety; the breed is smaller and neater than the Orpington.

CAMPINE Light Breed White Egg Layer

The Campine is an ancient breed from Antwerp in Belgium which has a very attractive barring or pencilling on the feathers, although the neck is without markings. Bred in silver or gold, the Campine was used to produce Pencilled Hamburghs. More recently it has been used in the production of the first autosexing breed, the Cambar. Campine hens lay a good number of smallish eggs; they are lively, quite flighty beautiful birds that like to free range.

CROAD LANGSHAN Heavy Breed Brown Egg Layer

Croad Langshans were first imported into Britain by Major Croad from China where they are said to have originated in the Monasteries. Most common in black with a beautiful green tinge, there is also a rare white variety. They both have a single comb and lightly feathered legs and feet. Langshans lay deep brown eggs. There is also a Modern Langshan breed which has been developed along different lines.

DERBYSHIRE REDCAP Light Breed White Egg Layer

The Derbyshire Redcap originated in Britain, and is a sturdy breed. It has a distinctive large rose comb. Redcaps are brown in colour with feathers tipped in black.

DORKING Heavy Breed Cream Egg Layer

The Dorking is one of the oldest domesticated breeds. It is thought that the Romans introduced a similar bird. The Dorking is named after the town in Surrey and various breeds were used to develop the Dorking into a dual purpose bird during the 19th century. The five toes are a distinctive feature. In the female, the single comb flops over to one side. Dorkings are large but have short legs. Colours vary from cuckoo to red, silver grey and white. Since February 2007 a 3m high silver version of the Dorking cockerel has stood on Deepdene roundabout at the town's eastern approach, ensuring that travellers are acquainted with the town and at least a little part of its history.

SOME LARGE FOWL HEAVY BREEDS

Rhode Island Reds

Light Sussex

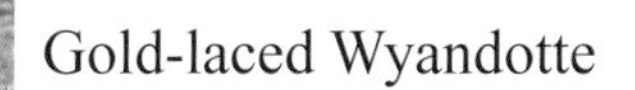

Gold-laced Wyandotte

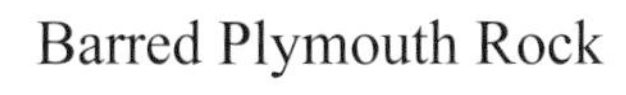

Barred Plymouth Rock

French Copper Black Marans

Barnevelder

Black Orpington

SOME LIGHT BREEDS

White Leghorn

Vorwerk

Partridge
Welsummer

Silver
Duckwing
Welsummer

Gold Silkie

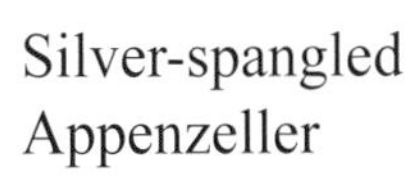

Silver-spangled
Appenzeller

BANTAMS

Buff Pekin

Gold Brahmas

Sablepoot

Friesian

Lavender Araucana

New Hampshire Red

HYBRIDS

Isa Warren

Black Rock

Amber Star

Speckledy

Left: Bluebelle
Right: Cream Legbar - an autosexing breed

FAVEROLLES Heavy Breed Cream Egg Layer

Faverolles originate from the village of Faverolles in Northern France and were created from a mix of several different breeds of hen, including the Dorking, Houdan and Cochin. Imported into the UK in 1886, producers of meat chickens crossed the Faverolles with the Sussex, Orpington and Indian Game. Although originally bred specifically for meat production, they also produce a good number of eggs and so are true dual-purpose birds. Colours vary from black, buff, cuckoo and ermine to salmon, which is probably the most popular. The birds have a broad, square body with small wings, a single upright comb, a striking beard and muffling. The pinkish legs are sparsely feathered and they have five toes. They are quiet, friendly birds that are ideal for children. The hens make very good broodies and mothers.

FAYOUMI Light Breed White Egg Layer

This is a rare Egyptian breed from the district of Fayoum (meaning water) south of Cairo. Fayoumis have been raised along the Nile since early times existing as free range scavengers. Fayoumis are hardy and good fliers so not ideal for small gardens. They are very attractive and can be silver or gold-pencilled. No other breed matures as quickly as the Fayoumi – pullets may start to lay small eggs at four months and the cockerels may start to crow at six weeks old!

FRIESIAN Light Breed White Egg Layer

The Friesian is a very rare breed originally from Friesland in Holland. Friesians are very small despite being large fowl, upright in stance and have single combs. They are pretty and can be gold-, silver- or chamois-pencilled.

HAMBURGH Light Breed White Egg Layer

Nobody knows where the Hamburgh originated – Holland, the UK or Germany have all been suggested. Hamburghs are rose-combed with slate legs and small with long bodies. They are available in attractive colours – gold, silver or black. The gold and silver can be pencilled or spangled. The bantams are miniature versions of the large fowl. Hamburghs are lively, active birds and difficult to tame because they are quite flighty.

KRAIENKÖPPE Light Breed White Egg Layer

The Kraienkoppe rare breed, also known as Twentse, originating on the border between Germany and Holland. It has increased in popularity recently and bantams are available.

LAKENVELDER Light Breed White Egg Layer

It is unclear whether this breed originated in the Netherlands or Germany. The Dutch claim the Lakenvelder was named after the village of Lakenvelt. Others think that the name came from Lakenvel, meaning shadow on a sheet and still others say the breed was named after Lakenvelder cattle which have black heads and tails and white over the rest of their bodies. But it is generally believed that the breed originated in the Westphalian area of Germany. Lakenvelders are striking with their white feathered long bodies contrasting with black neck and tail feathers; this colour marking is called belted. They are non-sitters and flighty, not liking to be cooped up.

MARSH DAISY Heavy Breed Tinted Egg Layer

The Marsh Daisy is a rare British breed which was popular in the 1920s. It was created in the 1880s by a Mr Wright in Southport. Old English Game, Malays, Hamburghs, Leghorns and Sicilian Buttercups were used in the creation of the breed. Colours vary from white and black to wheaten and buff. They are good foragers, go broody easily and are good mothers.

MINORCA Light Breed White Egg Layer

The Minorca probably originated in Spain and used to be very popular since it was a prolific layer of very large eggs. Minorcas have large white ear lobes and there are black and white versions. The hen has a large single comb which drops down over her face.

NORFOLK GREY Heavy Breed Cream Egg Layer

The Norfolk Grey originates from the town of Norwich, in Norfolk. The breed was created by Fred Myhill before the First World War as dual purpose birds under the name Black Marias. The name was reminiscent of funerals and was quickly dropped and the breed took the name Norfolk Grey instead. Although classed as a heavy breed, birds are not actually that large. They were developed by crossing the Birchen English Game with duckwing Leghorns. They have a single comb and legs are slate or black. Cockerels have silver white feathering with black striping on the neck, with the rest of the body being black; hens are predominantly black with silver lacing on the neck and breast. The Norfolk Grey is an excellent forager and does well when free ranging.

POLAND Light Breed White Egg Layer

The Crested Dutch or Polish breed was imported from Eastern Europe and in England renamed as Poland. The Poland has a long history going back to the 12th century. It is an ornamental small breed laying predictably tiny eggs. Its most striking feature is the crest of feathers on top of its head – the most popular variety is the white-crested black Poland. Polands can be flighty and are scared easily; they find it difficult to see as the crest partially covers their eyes. It is recommended to trim some of the feathers round their eyes. Polands are non-sitters. They can with patience be tamed. There is a new variety the Frizzled Poland that has come from Holland.

SCOTS DUMPY Light Breed White Egg Layer

Despite being bred in Scotland for over a hundred years and the fact that the Scots Dumpy had probably been around much longer than that, this breed nearly became extinct. Originally known as Crawlers and Creepers because of their very short legs, other names for them include Go-Laighs and Bakies. Fowls of this description were described as early as 1678 in Britain. S Scots Dumpies were used by the Picts as ambush alarms because of their superior hearing; their short legs and inability to wander too far made them perfect free rangers for Scottish crofts. Scots Dumpies are available as large fowl and bantams most commonly in black.

SCOTS GREY Light Breed White Egg Layer

An old breed, the Scots Grey was used on the isolated crofts in Scotland to provide meat and eggs. It is a rare breed outside Scotland. The steel grey colour with metallic black barring is distinctive.

SICILIAN BUTTERCUP Light Breed White Egg Layer

You can't miss a Sicilian Buttercup, which has an amazing saucer-shaped cup comb. Imported to Britain in 1912 by Mrs Colbeck of Yorkshire as a good layer, it was popular in the Sixties but is now rare. It is only available in gold or silver.

SPANISH Light Breed White Egg Layer

Specifically known as white-faced black Spanish, this is a Mediterranean breed, with large white ear lobes, flop-over comb and wattles.

SULMTALER Heavy Breed Cream Egg Layer

The Sulmtaler is a pretty, hardy breed from Austria. Birds are docile, easy to handle and hens are good layers of cream eggs.

THURINGIAN Light Breed White Egg Layer

A rare breed from Germany arriving in 2000 in bantam size, the Thuringian is bearded; colours are chamois-spangled or black.

TRANSYLVANIAN NAKED NECK Heavy Breed Cream Egg Layer

The Transylvanian Naked Neck breed originated in Hungary in an area which is now in Romania. Noted for its sparseness of feathers, with none on its bright red neck, it is rather an ugly bird but hardy; an excellent forager and a good layer. Due to its likeness to a turkey it has been known as Churkey. In France they are, to their misfortune, one of the main breeds for the broiler industry.

HYBRID HENS

The hybrids have become increasingly popular over the last few years as a great choice for families who want a few hens in their garden. They are ideal beginners' birds. Hybrids are developed by professional crossings of two specific breeds to obtain hens with the best egg laying capacity; the pure breeds used for this are predominantly Rhode Island Red, Sussex, barred Plymouth Rock, Leghorn and Marans. Hybrid hens are always first crosses and their parents are of different breeds or strains. Female chicks are reared for sale but all male chicks are killed. The crossing are sex-linked which means that males and females can be told apart by the difference in colour when hatched. Hybrids do not breed true which means you won't be able reproduce the same hybrids from your own.

The most popular hybrids which are readily available from agents/breeders are: ISA Warren, Black Rock, Speckledy, Bluebelle, Amber Star, Black Star, Sussex Star, Silver Link or White Star, Skyline (Columbine).

Hybrids were first developed in America in the 1940s to satisfy the huge growth in demand for eggs and meat. Thus the qualities of the best pure breeds were combined to produce prolific egg layers but also more recently they have been bred for hardiness and docility, making excellent pets to keep in the garden. They don't tend to go broody which can be an advantage. Hybrid hens are large (with no bantam versions available). The hens are sold by agents across the country and often two are sold as part of a starter pack which includes a hen house. The other advantage of hybrids is that they are vaccinated as chicks against a range of poultry diseases including Salmonella, Mareks Disease, Coccidiosis, Newcastle Disease, Infectious Bronchitis and Mycoplasma Gallisepticum. These vaccinations take place as the chicks grow over a period of 16 weeks.

Most brown egg laying hybrids are based on the Rhode Island Red while white egg layers are based on the Leghorn. Hybrids such as Black Rock, Bluebelle or ISA Warren which is similar to a commercial laying brown hen but bred for free range are all good choices for the garden. The hybrids are good beginners' birds as they have been bred to be friendly, sometimes too friendly! They are also an excellent size for the garden, in my opinion – not too small and not too big. Bantams are often really quite tiny and lay very small eggs; some of the large fowl pure breeds tend to be pretty big. Hybrids can lay upwards of 300 eggs a year for the first two years but eggs will diminish after this and hens may do as pure breeds do and take the winter off.

ISA WARREN

ISA Warrens, also known as ISA Browns, Lohmann Browns, Gold Stars or Goldlines are probably the most friendly and tame of all breeds. They are all the same ginger colour with flecks of cream streaked through their neck and tail feathers. They are produced by crossing a Rhode Island Red (gold) cockerel with a Light Sussex (silver) hen. This is called sex linkage with a gold and silver crossing. Males chicks will all be yellow (silver) and female chicks will all be brown (gold). Male chicks can be disposed of and female chicks reared and distributed for sale. They can be bought at POL (Point of Lay – this means they are around 18 weeks old and should be ready to start laying). They will lay around 320 brown eggs in their first year. These brown hens can be rescued at 18 months and are then known as Ex-caged Hens (they will have been laying intensively for just over a year and will have been rescued from the enriched cage systems by hen rescue organisations).

I had two ex-bats who lived until four years of age. I was lucky – they were healthy birds and continued to lay well. They were fearless (didn't blink an eyelid when we had a Springer Spaniel to stay) and very adventurous especially in the snow. They were always the first ones to the back door and would come straight in if given the chance. Isa Warrens are the least expensive of the hybrids. Columbian Blacktails, also known as Calder Rangers, also come under this category – they are similar in colour to ISA Warrens except that they usually have black tail feathers. They are often the favoured type for commercial egg laying free range flocks.

BLACK ROCK

Black Rocks are bred from selected strains of Rhode Island Reds and barred Plymouth Rocks. Peter Siddons of Muirfield Hatchery in Scotland acquired the breeding stock from breeders in America in 1973. He has been the sole breeder since then but has now handed over the reins to Eddie Lovett in Renfrewshire. The gold feathered genes of the Rhode Island Red are crossed with the silver feathered lines of the Plymouth Rock which produces a sex linkage feature that identifies each sex when the chicks hatch. The female chicks are sent out to the agents who bring them on and sell them at POL. Black Rocks have a good covering of feathers, which protect them in all weather conditions. They also have a highly developed immune system and seem to be less prone to red mite than other breeds. Black Rocks do not go broody as this trait has been bred out of them and although egg production is fantastic in the first two years, it may decrease thereafter. They should lay around 260 eggs in their first year which works out at five eggs per week. The Black Rock is one hybrid that does manage to go on producing eggs into its third, fourth and even fifth years but usually doesn't live beyond six or seven years of age; there are exceptions of course. They also produce good strong egg shells and this reduces the chances of egg peritonitis which so often occurs in battery hens and some other commercial hybrids. Black Rocks are black with ginger lacing. In my experience Black Rocks have a very inquisitive nature and are clever at getting into places that are out of bounds. Similar hybrids include the Bovans Nera and Rhode Rock.

SPECKLEDY

The Speckledy is increasingly popular – she is a hybrid based on a Cuckoo Marans and a Rhode Island Red. Resembling a Cuckoo Marans with slightly lighter feathering, she is a better layer, also producing dark brown eggs but they won't be as dark as that of the pure Marans. The Speckledy is docile, a great character, loves free ranging and making nests in strange places. She shouldn't go broody (although some do) and will lay around 270 eggs a year.

BLUEBELLE

The Bluebelle is a hybrid developed from a copper blue Marans/Rhode Island Red cross. The Bluebelle brand name is owned by Meadowsweet; other companies distribute similar birds, usually with Blue in the name. Bluebelles are placid, friendly birds. Their colouring is known as blue but is in reality grey, with a darker grey on the neck feathers. They are pretty and will look very attractive in your garden. They are good layers of approximately 260 brown eggs per year in their first two years; they particularly love to help with digging in the vegetable patch and will be the first to grab any worms that come to the surface. A healthy hybrid should live five or six years and may continue to lay in the spring and summer in her twilight years.

AMBERLINK aka AMBER STAR

The Amber Star is a recently developed hybrid from a reverse crossing of Rhode Island Red hen with a Rhode Island White cockerel, not to be confused with White Stars which are Leghorn-based hybrids. Amber Stars are docile, chunky birds with an inquisitive nature; they love to free range and should lay around 300 light brown eggs per year. Amber Stars are a slight exception to the rule that white feathered birds lay white eggs – this breed was developed with white feathers flecked with reddish brown because the original breeders claimed that feather pulling was less of a problem with white feathered birds due to the under-feathers being pretty much the same colour as the outer feathers. The birds are white because the Rhode Island White cockerel gives silver dominant genes.

WHITE STAR

This is a Leghorn-based hybrid that will lay white eggs. Leghorns are light birds and tend to be quite flighty so it follows that the hybrid may have a similar trait. She also tends to be smaller than the other hybrids. The White Star may well have large combs which flop over as in the pure breed Leghorn. Hens are prolific layers of at least 300 eggs in their first year.

SKYLINE

The hybrid version of the Araucana and layer of blue eggs is known as the Skyline, Columbine or Jasmine (commercial names depending on the originating poultry company). Skylines have crests and sometimes flop over combs. These hybrids have an 80% chance of laying blue eggs. Colours and markings vary - some are creamy coloured while others are darker with ginger/grey/red feathers. In my experience, they seem to be hardy, good free rangers, sometimes flighty and layers of around 250 eggs per year.

BOTH HYBRIDS AND PURE BREEDS HAVE ADVANTAGES AND DISADVANTAGES

Hybrid advantages	**Pure breed advantages**
Lay well for 2 years	lay for longer
Don't go broody	cockerels available so breeding possible
Lots of suppliers	you will be preserving a breed
Available all year	will have a breed club
Not expensive - around £15	pretty/more choice
Friendly	broodiness – raise chicks
Vaccinated against	
major poultry diseases	you can show/exhibit them
Medium sized	

Disadvantages	**Disadvantages**
Can be bullies	expensive - at least £25
Colourwise bit dull	no eggs in winter
No preserving of breeds No cockerels available	difficult to source the rare breeds
Won't breed true	can seem too big (large fowl) or too small (bantam)

AUTOSEXING BREEDS

In case you get offered some Cream Legbars or Rhodebars here is some information on these breeds:

Autosexing is the practice of breeding chicks, which can be sexed as soon as they hatch by their differing down colouring. The autosexing breeds are pure breeds (i.e. they breed true) so whichever way they are crossed, father to daughter, mother to son etc, males and females can be distinguished at birth. Sex-linked birds (i.e. hybrids) are different – Rhode Island Red (gold) can be crossed with light Sussex (silver) and the chicks can be sexed at birth but this will not work for the second generation.

There are various autosexing breeds that have been developed, their names ending in –bar. The first of these was the Cambar and was a cross between the Gold Campine and the barred Plymouth Rock. The barring is sex-linked and there is a double dose in the male and a single dose in the female – this means the male chick is paler with a blurred pattern of markings and a large yellow dot on top of its head; the female chick is darker with a stripe running from its head down its back. The barred Plymouth Rock is always used in the crossings to give the difference in colour.

Recognised breeds are the Gold, Silver and Cream Legbar (the Cream Legbar is a crossing which involves the Araucana and therefore lays blue eggs); the Rhodebar (from Rhode Island Red); Welbar (from Welsummer) and Dorbar (from Dorking). The Wybar uses the laced Wyandotte with the barred Plymouth

Rock and is most commonly in silver but they are rare. The Brussbar is also rare and is the autosexing version of the Brown Sussex. The crested Cream Legbars have been used to breed a blue egg-laying hybrid called Columbine or Skyline. These birds are typically reddish brown partridge feathered, some with crest and some without. They usually have quite a large comb but the probability of blue egg colour from these hybrids is usually 85%. There is also now a Silbar (from a Silkie).

The most popular is: **CREAM LEGBAR Blue Egg Layer**

The autosexing version of the Araucana is the popular Cream Legbar; this is a pure breed (from crossings of brown Leghorn, barred Plymouth Rock and Araucana). The Cream Legbar has a crest and females are a cream and grey with a salmon breast; cockerels are good-looking but can be aggressive. Colours are similar to the Skyline hybrid so sometimes the two get confused.

RESCUE HENS

Hens rescued from commercial egg farms are still known as Ex-Batteries (although strictly speaking battery cages are now enriched cages). Alternatives for rescue are ex-free range hens. Rescue hens become available to be rescued every year as farmers send them for slaughter after a year's laying. They are normally available for free or for a small donation.

These are not ideal beginners' birds since they need special treatment to start with and can have health problems. But if you don't mind the risk it and are lucky with your allotted hens it can be very rewarding. Ex-battery hens can be rescued from the British Hen Welfare Trust (www.bhwt.org.uk) – they have co-ordinators all over Britain. Other non-profit organisations are: Hen Rehomers (www.henrehomers.net) – they also have widespread co-ordinators, which means they have pick-up points across the country; Little Hen Rescue (www.littlehenrescue.co.uk) which is based in Norfolk and Free at Last (www.free-at-last.org.uk) based in Bedfordshire. The rescued hens may have lost a substantial amount of feathers and may not be strong enough to fly up on to a perch or into a nest box initially.

They will invariably have been debeaked and so will find it more difficult to pick up food. The tip of the beak will probably not grow back at this stage. Caged hens will have large combs, often flopping over to one side which will be very pale and anaemic looking compared to a free range laying hen whose comb will be bright red. The combs become enlarged due to the heat in the battery units – they act as heat dissipaters. The hens will need a good sized hen house and run and should be confined for about a week so that they can build up strength and adapt to new surroundings. After that they should be given the chance to scratch, forage for food and have dust baths. If it rains they should be encouraged to take shelter.

If ex-caged hens are joining an established flock it is best to rescue hens that are not too badly defeathered as they will amalgamate with the other hens more easily. Hens with few feathers will need several months to recover their plumage.

Ex-caged hens should be fed growers pellets to start with as these contain lots of protein. They will have only been fed layers mash while caged but will quickly adapt to a new diet. Later on they can be given layers pellets or mixed poultry corn and will enjoy special treats. If in good health ex-caged hens should continue to lay every other day for at least another year.

Organic free range hens also become available to rescue after usually a 14 month laying period. They will generally look in better health than the battery hens; they may not have been debeaked and their combs will look a much more healthy bright red. Usually they will not be so badly defeathered although surprisingly may have lost quite a lot of feathers on their backs towards their tail. I have rescued some Columbian Blacktails from the commercial free range flocks which supply Waitrose. They are meant to have black tail feathers but in practice they do not look substantially different to battery hens in colour and looks.

CROSS BREEDS

Cross breeds are a random mixture of breeds – the Heinz 57s of the chicken world! They are usually very hardy, age well and remain incredibly healthy with a good immune system. Our oldest hen was a cross breed and survived 10 years. So if you are not too bothered about the type of chicken you want, they are an excellent alternative and will not be expensive. The only problem will be finding some available for sale. Of course you might inadvertently acquire one by being sold a supposed pure breed which turns out to be a cross breed; this can happen especially if you are bidding for a hen or two at the market!

SPACE, RUNS AND SHELTER

Your hens will appreciate as much space as you can give them and as much grass as possible. As a minimum, large fowl need two square metres each in an outside run. Bantams will obviously make do with less space.

The first thing you need to do is find out whether there are foxes in your area because this will affect what sort of housing and run you decide to use. At the same time you need to be thinking about how free range your hens are going to be. You may want to keep them entirely enclosed because you have parts of your garden and precious plants that you want to protect or may have to, if you live in an urban area and have a smallish garden. In this case Arks are a good option since they are usually on wheels and can be moved to fresh patches of grass every day or at least every few days. On the other hand you may want a hen house placed in an enclosed run or yard, in which case you need to think about fencing and whether you want to pay the extra expense to make it completely fox-proof.

To give you a general idea, fox-proof fencing needs to be at least 2m high with an overhang at the top to prevent the fox climbing over it, and needs to be dug into the ground to a depth of at least 30cm to prevent the fox digging under it. To be effective against foxes you need to buy chain link fencing as a determined fox will bite through ordinary chicken wire.

You might also consider building two runs or dividing a large run in half so that you can rest half the run while using the other half. This will allow grass to grow back and will help prevent the build up of parasites.

The other option is electric fencing – this will keep your hens enclosed and safe from foxes and the advantage to this is that you can move the fencing to new patches of grass. The best type is a Flexinet green electric netting – it is popular because it blends into the background. The electric net is essentially a very secure mesh made up of electrifiable polywires that will give a shock to any animal trying to get through. The spacings between the horizontal wires start off at 5cm increments for the first four spacings and increase thereafter making the nets suitable for bantam sized birds and above. The electric poultry netting is 105cm high and contains 12 electroplastic twines with 11 being conductors. These nets are ideal for free range chickens and come with 15 single posts and the roll is 50m long. This form of fencing will set you back somewhere in the region of £70. You will also need a fencer unit (energiser) which could cost you around £100. Naturally you may not want to go down this route if you have small children or other family pets.

If you do not have foxes in your area (you are extremely lucky) then a less expensive option would be to use black plastic fruit netting around your run and to lock your hens into a secure hen house each night. The netting should keep your hens in and away from your vegetable garden if that is your aim.

If you have a large garden or field and want your hens to be completely free range you need only a secure hen house in which to close them up every evening and let them out every morning. If you do have a large garden and allow your hens to roam freely you will have very happy hens and you will be giving them the perfect existence and one that they deserve in exchange for laying you their perfect eggs.

If you grow vegetables, salads, etc, you should be warned that hens can very quickly ruin a vegetable patch. They particularly like spinach and all forms of lettuce – if you are going to give them the run of the garden you'll need to net susceptible vegetables (more of this later). However, your hens can be a useful addition to the garden – they are very good at breaking up the soil after you have dug over your vegetable garden in the winter; they forage for pests and produce droppings, which are one of the best fertilisers you can get. My chickens love following me around when I am digging the vegetable garden and are practically under my fork as I turn the soil and they grab the worms. You should also allocate, if you can, a patch of bare earth where your hens can enjoy their dust baths (more of that later).

If you want to prevent your hens flying out of a run or garden then you may want to clip their wings. The lighter breeds such as Leghorns are extremely good at flying. You will need to cut back the primary feathers on one wing only so that the hen will be unbalanced and unable to fly. As a general rule you need to clip the first three or four flight feathers back to half length. (for more on 'wing clipping' see page 89). On heavy breeds this should prevent them getting more than a few inches off the ground but the lighter breeds will still be able to fly up to 2m even with one wing clipped.

Whether your hens are free ranging or are enclosed they will still need somewhere to shelter during the day from wind and rain and from the sun in the summer. If there are no available trees, hedges or bushes then you may need to raise your hen house off the ground so that they can shelter underneath it.

MAKING A HENHOUSE

Introduction

If you are willing to raid skips for wood, speak to friends or neighbours who may have spare wood due to building work or have some old wood in the garage, you can probably build a hutch at little or no cost. You just need to be willing to put in a day's work to make it happen.

Chickens do not require a luxury boudoir in which to live. If you are making one 'for free', whilst you might hope it will last 100 years, with a little maintenance it can easily last 10 years before you have to build another or do some substantial repairs.

Some ground rules

Chickens need a hutch that is secure against predators, the main one being the fox but badgers are happy to take your birds if they can get in. The hutch needs to be waterproof and windproof and also needs natural ventilation as on hot days/ evenings the hutch can become particularly smelly and noxious as your hens will poop a great deal at night and their droppings contain ammonia.

The first thing that dictates the size of the hutch is the number of birds you have. The hens will sit happily on a perch side by side so a rough rule of thumb is that each medium sized bird needs about 30cm of perch space; for two birds the perch should be 60cm long. If you wish to put in more perches, they should be about 60-80cm apart. You will also have to consider your nest boxes, how many you need and where in the hutch to put them.

Before you begin, it is vital that you decide if the hutch will need to be moved and if the answer is yes, how often and by whom. If you need to move the hutch frequently, you should consider building a lightweight one and add handles or wheels to help with any movement.

My husband has built a number of heavy hutches but for a small/medium sized hutch he used a wooden delivery pallet which gives a sturdy and strong base from which to work. As the size of pallets can vary, he has taken the standard UK size (1200mm x 1000mm) as the basis for this DIY description of how to build a hutch and he has broken the process into a series of steps:

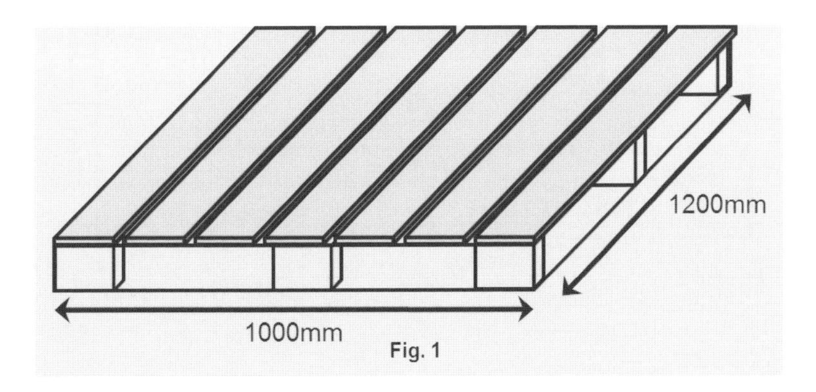

Fig. 1

You will need to decide the height of the sides and whether you want a ridge (as in a house) or a sloping flat roof. Consideration for the thickness of the wood is also important. If you are not diving in and out of skips and using what you can find, 12mm plywood is a good thickness, it is easy to cut and not too heavy.

Step 1

You will need to buy 3 x sheets of 12mm Plywood 2400mm x 1220mm and the cutting plan for each sheet is shown below. By cutting out all the wood you need at the start to the sizes specified, you will then be able to put the parts together like a jigsaw puzzle.

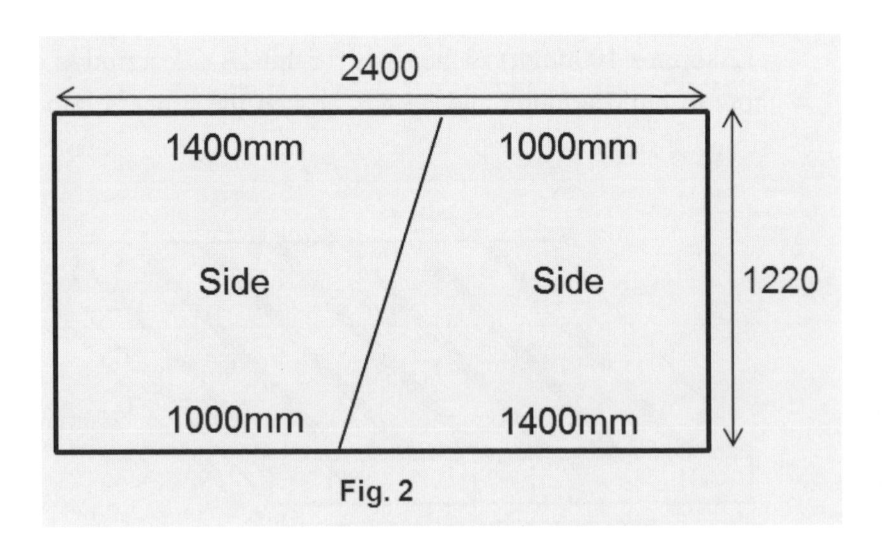

Fig. 2

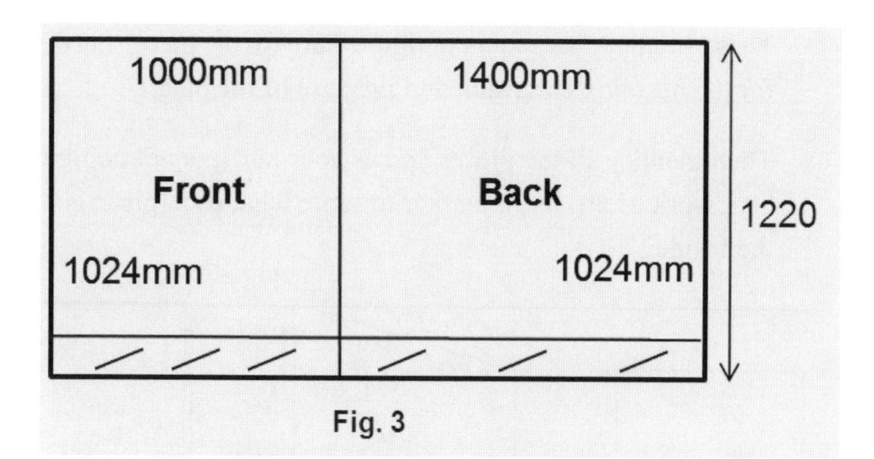
1000mm
1400mm
Front
Back
1220
1024mm
1024mm
Fig. 3

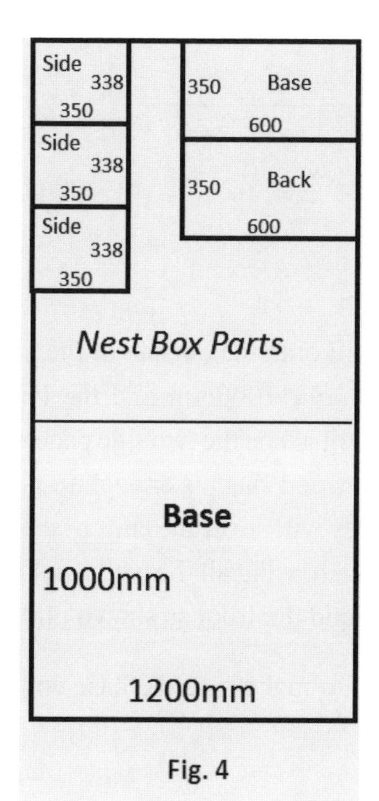
Side
338
350
Side
338
350
Side
338
350
350
Base
600
350
Back
600
Nest Box Parts
Base
1000mm
1200mm
Fig. 4

These smaller cuts shown in figure 4 are for the pieces needed for the nest box extension and the base of the hutch.

Then identify all the pieces and as your hutch is not going to be a work of art, use a marker to write what each piece is on the inside.

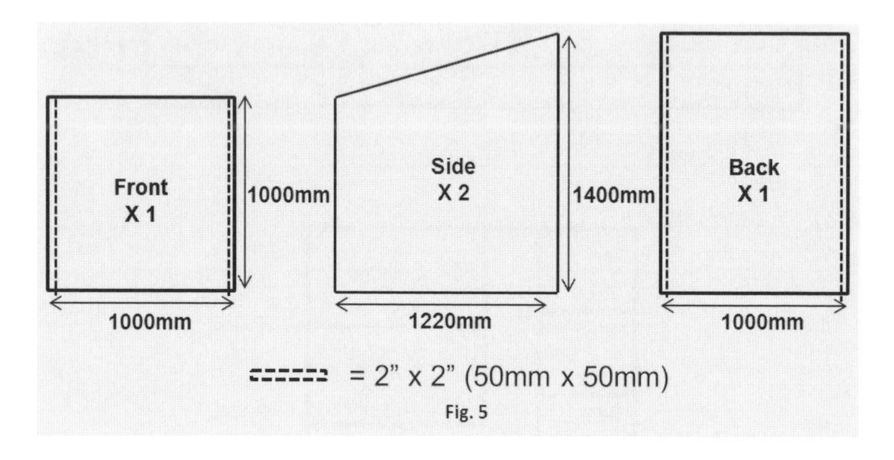

Fig. 5

All the panels will fit onto the outside of the pallet. The front needs to be 1000mm x 1000mm and the back 1000mm x 1400mm. They will fit inside the two side panels. Conveniently the width of the plywood sheet is enough to give the sides an overhang so that they will cover the ends of the front and back panel. To assist with bracing all the walls, put 50mm x 50mm batten on the back and the front as shown on figure 5.

You will also need to make sure the base covers the slats of the pallet.

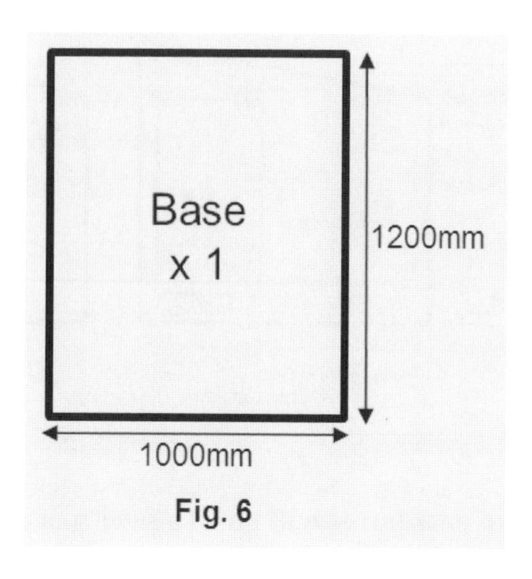

Fig. 6

Step 2

Before you start building the hutch you need to decide:

Where the door and where the pop hole will be. The door will allow you access to clean out the hutch (even crouching down it will be a squeeze). The pop hole will need to be either a portcullis type hatch or a simple hinged door with a bolt for a lock. For medium and large hens 300mm high x 220mm width is ideal for the pop hole or hatch.

Where the perches will go. Decide if you need one or two perches. Perches must be higher than the nest box as hens will roost as high as possible and if there is no distinct difference, they will roost in the nest boxes, creating a mess. Screw the supports for the perches onto the sides (the insides!) and using 18mm x 100mm plank cut two lengths 1000m long.

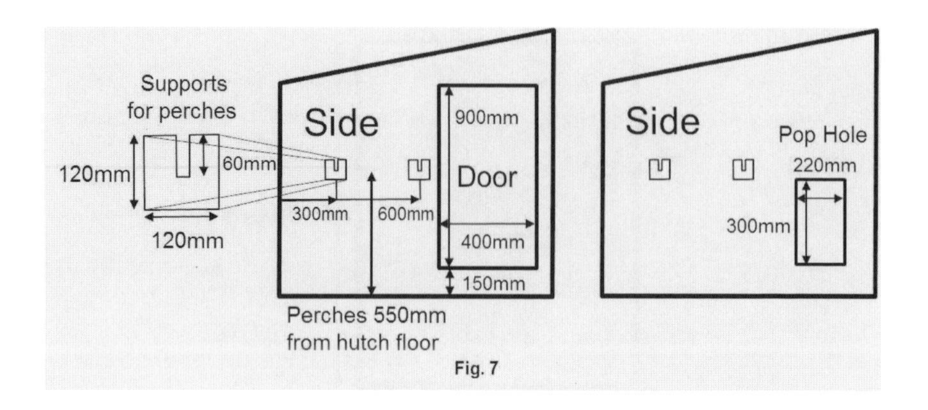

Fig. 7

Where the nest boxes will go. To save space in this size of hutch it is best to make the nest boxes protrude from the rear of the hutch as an 'extension'. This also means you can get at the eggs by using a lift-up flap.

Nest Boxes. The separate and detachable nest boxes (Fig. 8) should be off the floor of the hutch by about 250mm (approx 300mm from the ground) and the two compartments should be about 300mm wide each (600mm across the front) x 350mm deep x 300mm high.

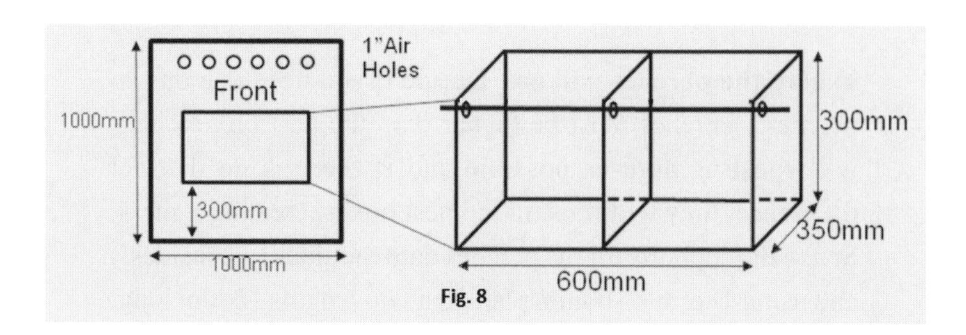

Fig. 8

If we look again at the nest box parts, the back has an extra 12mm because it will fit on the outside of the base. You might also want to consider using a batten, as seen before, to screw the two pieces together. This would mean cutting out a notch on each of the side panels as shown in figure 9.

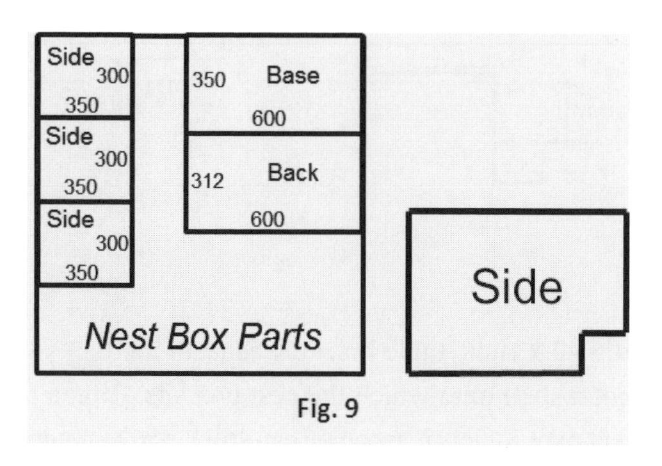

Fig. 9

Carefully cut out the hole in the front board 350mm x 300mm. Try to give about 1mm extra all the way round so that the nest boxes fit in with no bother. It should be central and 300mm from the base. Attach the off-cut by 2 x hinges to the bottom of this panel so you have made a door.

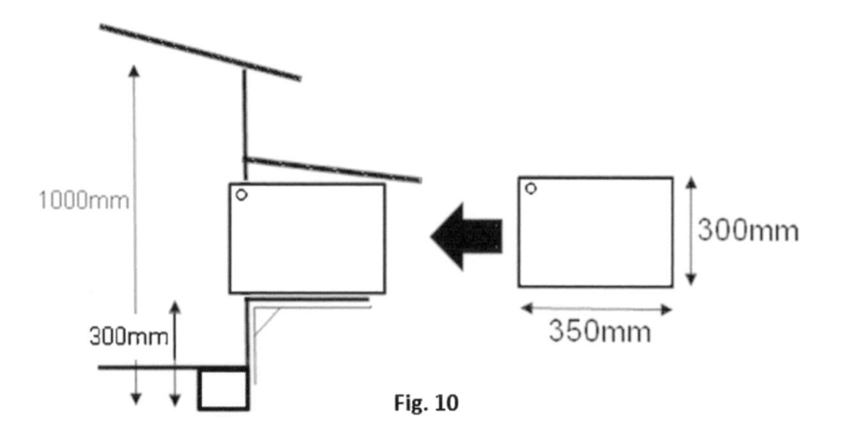

Fig. 10

By fitting 2 x right angle brackets beneath the flap you have then got a shelf onto which the nest box sits. If you remove the nest boxes for any reason you can still keep the hutch secure by lifting the shelf/door and securing it in place. Having made the nest box it connects and is held in place by two pieces of dowelling which is inserted through the side of the hutch and through the three holes in the top of the nest box.

Don't forget to cut a small window on one side of the hutch for ventilation and cover it with chicken wire.

Tools required

- Jigsaw with blades
- Hand saw

- Hammer
- Power or hand saw
- Tape measure
- Pencil and Steel ruler

Shopping list

- 3 x 12mm boards 2400mm x 1220mm.
- Approx. 5.5m of 50mm x 50mm wood to be used as battens.
- 2 x Roof sheets 2000mm x 950mm (Onduline or Coroline) (£15.00 each) or a roll of roofing felt.
- 1 x piece of dowelling 18mm x 1000mm.
- 1x plank 18mm x 100mm, two lengths 1000m long.
- 2 x heavy duty right angle (London) brackets.
- Paint - the better quality the paint the longer it will last before you need to repaint.
- Screws.

Putting the hutch together – a suggested sequence.

1. Cut out the nest box hole in the front panel and make the nest box as described above. Ensure they fit together well. Do not fit the right angle brackets at this stage.

2. Cut out the door in one side and cut out the pop hole in the other. In both cases fix the two doors into place using hinges, bolts and keepers.

3. Measure the two sides and fit the perch brackets.

4. Check the base fits on top of the pallet without overhanging and then screw the base to the pallet.

5. Screw the battens to the front and back.

6. Fit together all the outer panels using wood screws.

7. Fix the right angle brackets to the front panel and attach the nest boxes.

8. Screw the perches to the perch support brackets.

9. Paint the chicken hutch. You will need to use a primer on the wood first and then an undercoat and finally an outdoor gloss in whatever colour you like.

Roof Structure

There are many different ways to make the roof structure. Using Onduline or Coroline is recommended, but roofing felt can work too. If you use Onduline or Coroline, the simplest way to do it is to nail two battens to it that will fit on the inside of the panels of the hutch as shown in figure 11. The Onduline or

Coroline should be rigid enough however if you find that it lacks rigidity, you may need to attach some more battens to strengthen it up.

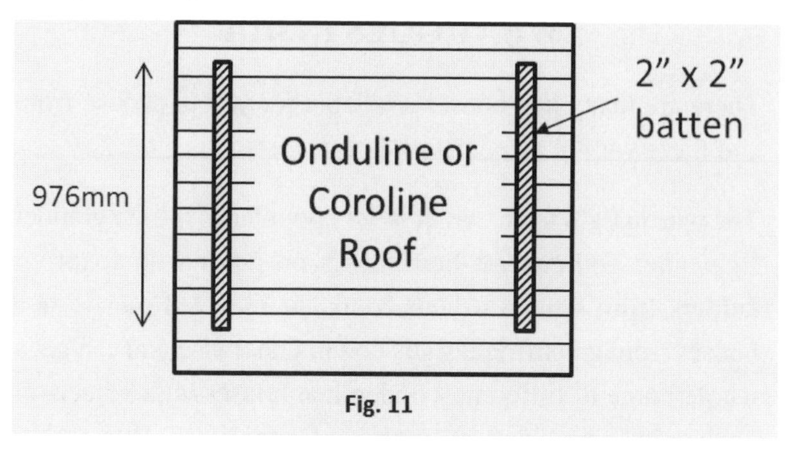

Fig. 11

If you wish to use roofing felt instead, you can do a similar thing but you will need an additional board on which to mount the felt and you can then attach the battens to this board. To stick the roofing felt to the board, you can use small nails and roofing felt adhesive for a strong bond. Fold the felt underneath the board for a tidy finish. It is also recommended that you use the felt adhesive to seal around the outside of the roofing felt to stop moisture and red mite (see page 115) getting underneath it.

After you have made the roof, it is a good idea to drill a hole through the battens and one of the side panels of the hutch so that you can put a pin through it which will help stop it blowing away in a strong wind. Alternatively, you can use hinges on the roof to allow you to open it easily or you can use a chain to hold it down.

BUYING A HEN HOUSE AND WHAT GOES INSIDE

There are many hen houses available for you to choose from and these vary in size, materials and costs.

The plastic Eglu from Omlet is very popular as is their grander Eglucube. You can get hen houses on poles with foxproof ladders from housesforhens.co.uk, or recycled plastic hen houses from greenfrogdesigns.co.uk. Otherwise you can get a whole range of different wooden hen houses with wheels or on legs or arks from a number of suppliers. Remember ventilation is important and the house should be robust and weatherproof. You can even get the Nogg Hen house which is wooden and built in the shape of an egg with a glass top. It is expensive though and only houses two to four hens.

Bedding

There are various options for bedding that you can use in the hen house. Wood shavings or wheat straw are best – any moisture from droppings should get absorbed. Straw is cheaper but can result in feathers being stained. You can buy dust-extracted shavings and you can pay a bit more for chopped wheat straw. There is also a new bedding on the market called HempBed-E which is dust-free chopped hemp and has Eucalyptus pellets added to freshen up the hen house. If you want to be economical, shredded paper can also be used but it may get deposited out of the hutch by scratching hens and as it tends to be white doesn't look very attractive. Some people use layers of newspaper successfully but this would need to be changed frequently. Hay should not be used as it harbours harmful mould spores that can cause breathing problems. All bedding should be changed once a week. I use straw in the nest boxes which the hens seem to like as they can make themselves a proper nest. Another option which will cost you nothing is to use dried leaves on the floor but you can only really utilise these for a few weeks in the autumn. If you can store them in a dry place once gathered they could last for quite a while. The leaves will form a sort of deep litter and when you come to clean them out, they will make an excellent addition to the compost heap. Whatever bedding you choose to use make sure it does not get damp as this can cause respiratory problems with your hens.

Perches

Chickens prefer to roost (sleep) sitting on a perch. In your chicken hutch you should have a piece of planed wood around 5 - 8cm thick and rounded off on the top edges set horizontally across the hutch. The height off the floor does matter as the hens will always roost as high up as possible. If you have an adapted garden shed as a hutch you will need to ensure the hens have an easy route up to the perch. If possible you should try and make your perches detachable, using slotted grooves so that you can clean them; the end of perches is a favourite spot for red mite to gather and multiply. If you have large hens such as Brahmas, Orpingtons or Cochins you will need low perches as they are not good flyers.

Nest Boxes

Nest boxes are essential for laying hens and should be a minimum of 40cm wide, 30cm deep and 40 cm high. One nest is needed for every four birds although often hens share the same nest box. Nest boxes should be bedded down with shavings or straw and have a lip to prevent straw and eggs rolling out. Free range hens will most likely find their own nesting spot which will be dry, dark, cosy and hidden away – it may be amongst undergrowth, in a sage bush, in a sack of leaves or compost or on a shelf in the garden shed.

FEEDING AND EQUIPMENT

A normal sized hen needs about 120g of food a day in the form of grain. This is a rough guide - hens like to eat small quantities throughout the day so food must be available to them at all times. Covered feed hoppers should be used so that the feed remains dry. All feed should be kept in dustbins or containers with lids to avoid the possibility of rats, mice or badgers getting to it. Feed is available from agricultural merchants in the form of mixed poultry grain, layers pellets or layers mash. Mixed grain consists of wheat, barley, oats and maize (the maize usually gets eaten first). Pellets and mash consist of ground poultry grain with various other ingredients added, including soya, essential fatty acids and methionine, an amino acid. Calcium and phosphorus are added which help towards strong egg shells plus vitamins and trace elements. Pellets are small and cylindrical – they are clean and easy for hens to eat. If your hens are confined all the time in a run they may get bored because they won't be able to do much natural foraging. Layers mash will keep the birds busy for hours because it is harder to pick up and can be fed dry or wet. The main problems with layers mash is that some of it can go to waste.

If your hens are confined but allowed to free range some of the time, layers pellets are a good option because they contain everything the hens need in their diet. Some people feed layers pellets in the morning and mixed grain in the evening. Layers pellets are often recommended because they are formulated to be a nutritionally balanced diet.

For free ranging hens, I am in favour of a more varied diet – like us, I think they thrive on a variety of foods. Hens are omnivores; our domestic hens are all descended from the red jungle fowl who would have survived on all the food available in a forest which would have included grains, green stuff, berries, insects and grubs and even small animals such as mice. I feed mainly mixed poultry corn. The hens love the maize which is said to be fattening – however my hens don't seem to be overweight and free range all day which keeps them fit and healthy.

There is no doubt that chickens thrive by eating grass; they eat the growing tips of grass which is at its best in the spring and early summer. Grass contains omega 3 fatty acids and also carotinoids which make the yolks such a lovely deep yellow. Your hens will also be searching amongst the grass for seeds and insects. All sorts of green weeds such as chickweed, dock and dandelion leaves will form a part of any free ranging hens' diet. Leafy green vegetables such as lettuce or any salad leaves, spinach, beetroot leaves, cabbages and Brussels sprouts will all be devoured by your hens. If you have a vegetable garden you can give them all your surplus vegetables. They particularly like Jerusalem artichokes and courgettes (if you have overgrown or surplus courgettes, cut them in half and your hens will enjoy the seeds as well as the courgette flesh). Chickens enjoy grubs and insects they find in the garden such as: worms, slugs, snails (crushing the shell makes it easier for the hens to eat the snail and they will eat the shell which is a good source of calcium), woodlice, earwigs, beetles, ants, flies if they can catch them (some of my hens will eat dead flies!). They don't seem to eat caterpillars. They might also eat frogs and small mice.

It is no longer legal to feed kitchen scraps to hens, because of the risk to domestic animals from contaminated meat (infections such as the Foot and Mouth Disease virus can be spread by infected meat). This means you should not feed anything to your hens that has been prepared in your kitchen. You could however buy bread or vegetables in the supermarket and feed it directly to your hens.

Water

Fresh water needs to be available to chickens at all times. Each hen can drink at least 300ml of water per day. There are a number of different sized drinkers on the market made of either plastic or galvanized metal. Plastic drinkers are preferable in winter when the water freezes – the ice can be removed easily but they can crack quite easily especially in the cold. Galvanized drinkers need hot water to unfreeze the water inside them. However, they are more durable but also more expensive. Drinkers can become dirty with green algae and placing them in the shade will help prevent this. In any case stagnant, green water is not good for hens so water should be changed every other day. I find in the really cold weather it is best to use plastic bowls filled with fresh water, to bring them inside in the evening and to replenish frequently and you will need to break any ice that formed during the day. My hens seem to like eating crushed bits of ice!

Your chickens may well benefit from apple cider vinegar (ACV) which can be added to drinking water – just a quarter of a teaspoon in the drinker will be sufficient and only for one week per month. The vinegar acts as an all round health tonic. It aids digestion, keeps the gut healthy, helps discourage worms and keeps the feathers in good condition. This only works in a plastic drinker as in the galvanized steel type it dissolves the zinc which is poisonous to hens. Cider vinegar in the water also prevents the build up of algae in containers. An unpeeled clove of garlic can also be added to drinking water – garlic can boost the immune system.

Grit and Oystershell

Grit and oystershell should be available especially if your hens are confined. Flint grit is needed to grind up food in the gizzard as hens don't have teeth. The flint grit will remain doing its job in the gizzard for quite a while. Oystershell, which is also known as soluble grit is needed as it adds calcium to the hens' diet and helps in the production of the egg shell. Both grit and oystershell can be picked up from the soil and a chalky soil is especially good for the extra calcium. I put out mixed grit (contains flint grit and oysterhsell) so that the hens can peck at it ad lib. Vitamin D in the form of cod liver oil can be added to the feed if egg shells are thin. Vitamin D helps the absorption of calcium. Only a teaspoon at a time needs to be added; too much cod liver oil fed to your hens would result in the eggs tasting fishy.

FINDING AND BUYING YOUR HENS

Go to a reputable source and see your hens before you buy them. The Domestic Fowl Trust which is based in Worcestershire is worth a visit as you can take a good look at the variety of breeds. There are also Poultry Shows and Agricultural Shows (with poultry sections) held all over the country throughout the year where you can look at the different breeds. If you decide on hybrids you can find various companies through a search on the internet that advertise Point of Lay hybrid hens. Many breeders of the more traditional pure breeds also act as agents for the hybrid breeders. Country Smallholding has an excellent section of poultry breeders in the back of the magazine. Beware of buying your first hens at a livestock market – you may end up with four young cockerels. Or you may end up with less than healthy hens.

Things to look out for when looking at hens you want to buy:

1. A red comb, bright eyes and dry nostrils
2. Nice shiny feathers with no bare patches
3. Clean feathers around the vent – a dirty bottom can be a sign of ill health
4. Alert and active behaviour

You can expect to pay less for hybrids than pure breeds. Pure breeds are often sold in trios (a cockerel and two hens).

If you are buying pure breeds the best time to do this is late summer. At this time spring-hatched chicks are coming up to 20 weeks and breeders will have some on offer that they don't wish to keep. They will have selected what they need for breeding and showing. They will usually have surplus hens that are perfectly healthy and attractive but which may have breed faults such as feather colouring that is not quite right. You can also research the pure breeds and breeders by contacting the Breed Club for a breed you are interested in. There are about 50 Breed Clubs for the most popular breeds.

GETTING TO KNOW YOUR HENS AND OBSERVING WHAT THEY LIKE TO DO

Most people, especially families, want their hens to be reasonably tame and some breeds have naturally better temperaments than others. Hybrids are bred to be docile. The heavier pure breeds, especially the large Orpingtons, Brahmas and Cochins, tend to be reasonably tame; the lighter breeds and bantam versions, with the exception of the Pekin, will be more nervous and flighty. However most chickens can become tame if you spend time chatting and handling them and feeding special treats from your hand. Just sitting and watching them on a sunny afternoon will give you pleasure and help you get to know what they like doing. You will be constantly entertained by their antics as they all have different chracters.

Hens have many needs – apart from making nests and laying eggs, they love to exercise, flap their wings, preen, dust-bathe, sunbathe, scratch, peck and forage for food as well as perch off the ground during the day.

Handling your Hens

Catching your hens may not always be easy. Putting down some food may help. Some breeders use a fishing net to catch their birds as it can be placed gently over them when cornered. If you can, pick up a bird by placing both hands over its wings, then lift and place on your arm with its head facing backwards. The palm of you hand will rest under her breast and her legs can be held between your fingers. The other hand is free to place on his or her back to balance or examine the bird. Chickens should not be held upside down by either one or both legs.

Dust Bathing

If hens are confined, it is important that a dust bath is provided for them. A large box should be half-filled with dry earth, sand or ashes or you can mix all three together. If hens are free-ranging they will make dust baths for themselves in any areas of bare earth and craters will develop – dominant hens will often oust others from good dust bath spots. Chickens like to squat down and shake themselves with movements of the body and wings so that their feathers get covered in dust. The dust trickles through their feathers and onto their skin. In this way they clean themselves and the dust helps remove many of the parasites, such as lice, which infest the skin. Chickens also dust bathe in hot weather as a way of cooling down. Once finished, they will give their feathers a good shake and probably go back to searching for food.

Sunbathing

Chickens love the sunshine and delight in basking in it. You will find your hens sunbathing whenever there is some warm sunshine. They will lie on one side, spreading out their uppermost wing; they need their vitamin D just as we do.

Preening

Hens and cockerels preen themselves using their beaks at least once a day to sort out their feathers. They use a gland located at the base of the tail which produces a special oil secretion for the conditioning or preening of feathers. The oil is picked up in the beak and then distributed through the feathers. This oil in their feathers acts as a waterproof jacket, preventing rain from seeping through to the skin; it also acts as an insulator helping to keep chickens warm in cold weather.

Pecking Order

Pecking order is the word used for the hierarchy or ranking structure of a flock of hens and is established separately for the hens and for cockerels if there are more than one. A cockerel looking after a group of hens will be at the top of the pecking order. Hens under him will fight to be the second most powerful by pecking each other. If a hen loses a fight she will adopt a submissive pose, with her body lowered and legs bent. Incidentally, the larger a hen's comb is, the more dominant she will be in the flock and she will probably automatically gain second place in the pecking order. If there is no cockerel in the group, the hen with the largest comb will probably be boss and will take on a male role – she may even crow!

New hens introduced to an established group may take a while to achieve a pecking order – on the whole older hens will be more self-confident and expect a high rank while younger, more timid hens may go straight to the bottom of the pecking order. If you have two cockerels, one will become dominant, or you may find they fight, especially if they are enclosed and you may have to separate them. If you introduce new hens to an established flock you should isolate them for the first few days to avoid bullying problems. It must also be said here that often hens and bantams develop friendships just like humans - sometimes two or three hens will stick together during the day and at night.

General Pecking (also see Feather Pecking on page 111)

There are different forms of pecking that you can observe amongst your hens which do not necessarily have anything to do with the Pecking Order. Gentle feather pecking where one hen pecks at the tips of feathers on another bird or even pecks the plumage of the resident cockerel is not serious and does not result in feather damage; hens do, given the chance, like to eat feathers as they are full of protein. Hens are bound to peck at each other if they are bored, upset or challenged. If hens have plenty of room for foraging this does help to prevent feather pecking as they are kept busy pecking in the grass, leaves and earth. A broody hen, who comes off her eggs every day for food and water, will be very uptight, clucking and disgruntled; she may well peck any hens who cross her path or she may get pecked. Once her chicks are hatched she will be very protective and if eventually let out with the rest of your flock will aggressively peck any hen that comes near her brood. Chicks brought up under the care of mother hen have many benefits as she will teach them everything they need to know including the art of foraging and research has shown mothered chicks are less sensitive to fear and stress as a result – all this will mean they are less likely to indulge in the habit of feather pecking when they grow up.

A Typical Day

In the summer when there is plenty of light, a hen's day will start at sunrise with feeding and probably egg laying. After a hen has laid she often feels like some more to eat (all that hard work has made her peckish!). There follows a period during which hens will preen their feathers and clean the more inaccessible parts of their bodies with their beaks. My chickens tend to do this standing on top of their various hutches, especially in winter when the grass is wet. At about midday hens often like to relax in a dust bath and doze in a cool place if it is hot or in the sunshine.

Later on, a second peak of activity occurs in which the cockerel may be mating with his hens and, if not confined, all your hens will be out and about foraging for interesting food. They will also want to fill up their crops ready for the night. My hens always seem to graze on grass just before bed; a bit like us needing a hot chocolate or a nightcap before retiring. Hens like to sleep in groups on a perch in their houses or, like some of mine, roost up in a tree for the night. Pecking order is evident at this time because the hens who come first in the pecking order will want to sleep on the highest perches. Once they are settled, hens will retract their necks, tuck their heads away into their feather shut their eyes and go to sleep.

THE ANATOMY

PARTS THAT YOU SHOULD KNOW ABOUT

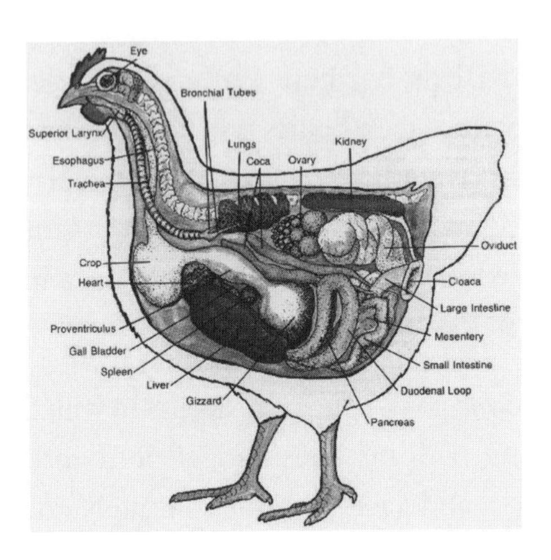

BEAK

The tip of a hen's beak is sensitive and tends to be quite sharp; it is important in foraging when pecking the growing tips of grass and pulling worms and other grubs from the earth.

Beak tipping or debeaking is actually quite a cruel practice but is common in caged hens as well as some commercial free range flocks. An infra-red beam is used which causes the beak tip to fall off; no anaesthetic is used and it is thought that the hen does suffer pain (this is not like a human cutting his or her fingernails). The top beak is therefore shortened leaving the bottom beak sticking out. This procedure is carried out to stop intensively-reared and some of the free range flocks from pecking and harming each other. The beak does not grow back and remains blunted. If you have hens that are confined sometimes the upper beak can grow overlong and you may need to cut it just a little - the bit that needs to be cut back is usually an obvious lighter colour. You can snip it off with a pair of straight nail clippers.

CLAWS

Occasionally claws need to be clipped. This shouldn't be a problem if your hens free range as scratching and foraging keeps the claws in good condition. With battery hens that have been rescued and have never had the opportunity to forage or scratch around in the earth, the claws can become too long. You can safely clip them back with a strong pair of nail clippers. Don't clip them back too much – if you hold the claw to the light you can see an internal blood vessel so make sure you don't cut through it!

COMB

Combs can vary greatly in size and shape between breeds. Combs and wattles are always bigger on the males, showing their dominance but is also a feature to attract the hens. The single comb is probably the most common but can be quite small in some breeds and very large in others; it is called a folded single or semi-erect single if it flops over. Rose and pea combs are also fairly popular; the rose comb, as seen on the Wyandotte, is flat on top but is covered with small points rather like a hairbrush. A pea comb is a triple comb with three single combs, distinctly divided but joined at the ends; the

Brahma has one of these. There are some very unusual combs such as the horn (seen on a Sultan), the cup (seen on a Sicilian Buttercup), the leaf (seen on a Houdan), and the mulberry (seen on a Silkie).

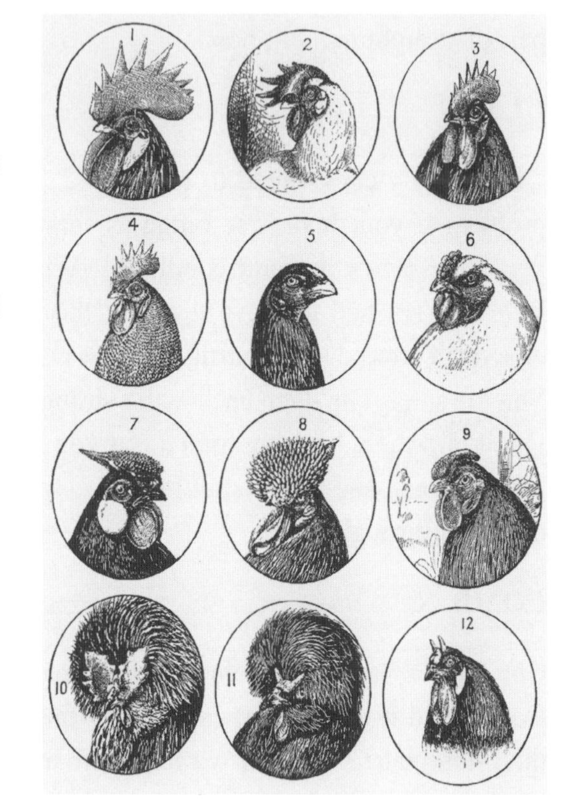

1. Single (cock)

2. Single (hen)

3. Single (small)

4. Single (high)

5. Undeveloped

6. Pea (triple)

7. Flat rose

8. Large rose

9. Curved rose

10. Leaf

11. Wide horn

12. Horn

CREST

The crest is a tuft of feathers on the head also sometimes known as the topknot. In Old English Game it is known as the Tassel. Araucanas have small crests; Silkies have slightly larger crests;

Polands have huge crests which come down over their eyes, often obscuring their view.

CROP

The crop is in the front of the hen below the neck. Food is stored in the crop before going down into the stomach in the first stage of digestion. Hens and cockerels have no teeth so food picked up by the beak is carried into the gullet by the tongue and from there goes into the crop. The crop is like a food store and can be quite large by the end of the day. Here grain etc is softened by saliva coming from glands in the mouth. Food passes from the crop into the stomach where gastric juices are released and is then transferred to the gizzard.

EARS AND EARLOBES

Chickens have a very good sense of hearing. Their ears are located near to their eyes but there are no pinnae or exterior ears showing. A few feathers will cover the ear opening. Chickens are capable of making lots of different noises when communicating with each other. Hens can hear their chicks cheeping in their shells and mother hens constantly call their chicks to food. Cockerels and hens will always alert each other through cackling to any dangers or threats from predators that they see. They will respond to human voices and can be taught to come when you call them. So keep chatting to your hens; you never know what they might understand! All chickens have earlobes located under the ear opening. As a general rule white egg layers will have white earlobes which look quite noticeable on the sides of their faces. Brown egg layers have red earlobes. There are a few exceptions Sumatras are black all over and this includes the earlobes. Minorcas, a Mediterranean breed, have huge white earlobes. Silkies have turquoise or mulberry earlobes.

EYES

Scientific research tells us that chickens have excellent vision and I can certainly back this up as a result of watching my hens during the day: dashing after flying insects; seeing me through the windows or door even when they're way up the garden; and spotting flying predators well before I do. With their eyes placed on opposite sides of their heads they have a panoramic vision of 300° compared to a human's forward facing vision of 180°. Chickens have a binocular vision (this is the field of view seen by both eyes) of only 26° whilst humans have 120°. Unlike humans though a chicken's eyeball is stationery so it has to move its head to follow objects. So basically a hen cannot see directly in front of her.

Since our domestic fowl have developed from wild chickens living in forests where their vision was limited by trees and undergrowth, their eyes are best focused for small objects up to five metres away but only for larger objects at about 50 metres distant. Consequently they are not usually happy to move more than 50 metres from their housing, which they like to keep in sight. To see things in three dimensions, chickens need to fix objects first with the left eye and then with the right. This is why you see their heads moving from side to side and they walk in a zigzag fashion.

Eyes are usually orange with a black pupil. Appenzellers have black eyes as do Silkies and Sumatras. The Bluebelle hybrid usually has a dark and quite prominent eye and some birds have green eyes.

Chickens are blessed with a third eyelid. Apart from the two eyelids that come together when a chicken shuts its eyes there is a nictitating, translucent membrane which is located next to the eyeball and slides from front to back. This membrane's function is to moisten, clean and protect the eye. It is particularly useful when dust bathing as it will protect the eye from dirt. Sometimes when you take a photo of your favourite hen its eyes will appear hazy or blurred because the membrane is being used – it's just one more hindrance to getting the perfect picture.

FEATHERS

Feathers cover almost all breeds of poultry with the exception of Silkies who are covered by down and of course there are no feathers on the neck of the Transylvanian Naked Neck. Feathers are shed during the moulting process in the autumn and new feathers sometimes of a slightly different shade will regrow reasonably quickly. The undeveloped feathers which form short stubs are known as pin feathers. Feathers on different breeds can have beautiful colours and patterns. Feathers can be: **barred** – alternate stripes of light and dark across the feather; **cuckoo** – irregular banding where two colours are difficult to distinguish and run into each other as on the Cuckoo Marans; **laced** – a stripe around the edge of a feather; **double-laced** – two layers of lacing, one on the outer edge of the feather and then an inner one – these could be black or brown; **pencilled** – small stripes going across on a feather or concentric following the outline of the feather; **spangled** – a spot of different colour at the end of each feather; **splashed** – a contrasting colour unevenly displayed on the feather; **mottled** – marked with tips or spots of different colour. Chickens' feathers on each hen have differing textures and size. Down-type feathers, also known as fluff, tend to cover the backside of many hens. The cockerel has hackles which are feathers on his neck, saddle and on his back just in front of the tail and sickles which are his long curved tail feathers. On the hen this area of feathers in front of the tail is called the cushion because of its softness.

Several breeds sport feathered legs and feet – the little Pekins have heavily feathered legs which prevent them from scratching up too much soil. Other breeds include the Cochin (large version of the Pekin), French Marans, Brahma, Faverolles, Sultan, Langshan, Barbu D'Uccle and Booted Bantam (Sablepoot).

GIZZARD

Hens have no teeth as previously mentioned, hence the saying "As rare as hens' teeth" so the gizzard which is down below the crop, has an important function. Food arrives here from the stomach. It is then ground up using grit that the hen has consumed expressly for this purpose.

HACKLES

Hackles are the neck feathers on hens and cockerels. The cockerel's neck hackles will be long and pointed as will his saddle feathers which are also called hackles. The saying, 'making someone's hackles rise' comes from a fighting cockerel whose hackles rise when he is angry.

LEGS

Legs are covered in scales which differ in colour depending on the breed. Most commonly legs are yellow but they can also be pink, a slate grey, black (as in the Sumatras) or green (as in Marsh Daisies). Scales can become infected with mite (see Scaly Leg Mite on page 116).

SPURS

Spurs consist of horny material and are an outgrowth of the leg bone, growing on the inside leg of the cockerel and are used for fighting. Aggressive cockerels will use these spurs against other cockerels or even against humans if seen as a threat. They have a core and an outer husk. Artificial metal spurs were used in cockfighting and were first introduced in the late 1600s. The cockerel's natural spurs were filed down and these metal spurs were attached with leathers around the legs as they would incur more serious injuries. Silver spurs, which were a softer metal, apparently proved less fatal than spurs of steel.

TAIL

Hens' tail feathers become very erect when they are in lay but it is these feathers which often get lost if a hen is being feather pecked. Hens' tail feathers can vary substantially in size depending on the breed. But it is the cockerels that have the most stunning varieties of tails. The Yokohama cockerel has amazingly long beautiful tail feathers which brush the ground. The rumpless breeds such as Rumpless Araucana and the Rumpless Game have no tail feathers! A squirrel tail is the name for feathers which are carried too high and a wry tail is carried to one side; both are defects in a cockerel which is intended for breeding or showing.

TOES

The majority of chickens have four toes but there are six breeds which have five. These are most famously the Dorking but also the Houdan, Faverolles, Silkie, Sultan and the Lincolnshire Buff.

VENT

The vent is the orifice at the back end of the bird through which the egg passes out but also through which excreta is expelled. The vent of a laying hen will be larger than a non-layer, moist and crescent shaped.

WATTLES

Wattles are the two red fleshy appendages hanging below the beak. Hens have small wattles, cockerels have much larger ones. The wattles are there to cool the chicken down – blood circulates from the comb to the wattles and lowers the bird's temperature during hot weather.

WINGS

Primaries or flight feathers are elongated and stiff to provide lift when a hen uses its wings to flap or fly. The secondaries are the inner quills on the wings. The axial feathers separate the secondary and primary feathers. If there is a problem with hens flying out of runs then wings can be clipped – only one wing on each bird and only the primary feathers should be clipped as the idea is to make flying impossible due to imbalance. Use kitchen scissors and cut about 7cm from where the quills go into the flesh – if one cuts too near the flesh the quills will bleed.

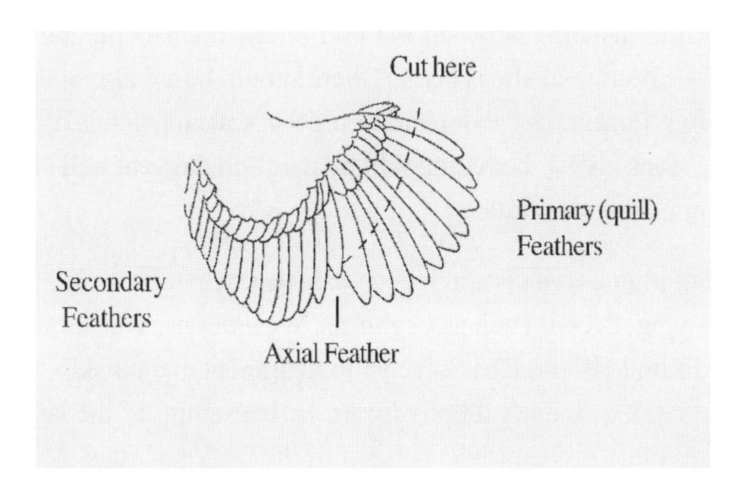

EGG LAYING AND THE ALL-IMPORTANT EGG

Pointers to an Egg Laying Hen

Your hybrid hens will come into lay between 18 and 22 weeks. Pure breed hens may start a little later than this. An easy pointer to a hen that is laying is a good-sized, red comb which is soft and warm to the touch. Laying hens will also have erect tails. On a more technical basis, you can pick her up and feel for her pelvic bones which should be about 5 cm or the width of three fingers apart. Her vent should be soft and moist. You can also test the distance between the end of the breastbone and the pelvic bones – if she is laying, there should be a width of three or four fingers. The abdomen should feel soft and pliable. When she stops laying, her comb will be pale and the vent will close to one finger's width.

Beak pigment in certain breeds can also help tell you if a hen is laying. Breeds such as Leghorns, Wyandottes, Welsummers and Rhode Island Reds have yellow pigment in their skin, legs and beak called xanthophylls. At the beginning of the laying period this pigment will be seen in the beak and legs. As the hen begins to lay, the pigment which is obtained from such food as yellow maize and green plants will now be required for the yolks. The pigment in the beak starts at the base when she is not laying. It will move up the beak and will be seen as a ring of pigment in the middle of her beak when she is laying.

It will then reach the tip of her beak and will gradually fade away as she continues to lay. When the pigment reappears at the base of the beak this means she has stopped laying.

Pre-laying behaviour

Hens, especially pullets, about to lay for the first time, may take a day searching out a nest site, visiting and investigating several potential spots before choosing one. They may spend some time preparing the nest, moving straw or similar with their beaks and hollowing out the spot. If a cockerel is present he may get involved, helping to suggest and preparing sites himself. Once a hen starts laying, she will also exhibit pre-laying behaviour about an hour before her egg is actually laid. She may, for example, queue up to lay in a popular nest box that is already being used, as hens quite like to use the same spot. Alternatively she may visit several suitable sites, sit for a bit and then change her mind until laying her egg reasonably quickly in the first place that she chose. Sometimes hens can be caught short and lay their eggs on the ground while going about other activities.

The Making and Arrival of the Egg

The yolk of the egg is formed in the ovary and is then released to travel down the oviduct. In the longest part of the oviduct much of the albumen is added and also the cord-like chalazae which keep the yolk in place. The egg is driven down by peristaltic squeezing movements to the isthmus where it receives the shell membrane. It then moves to the uterus (shell

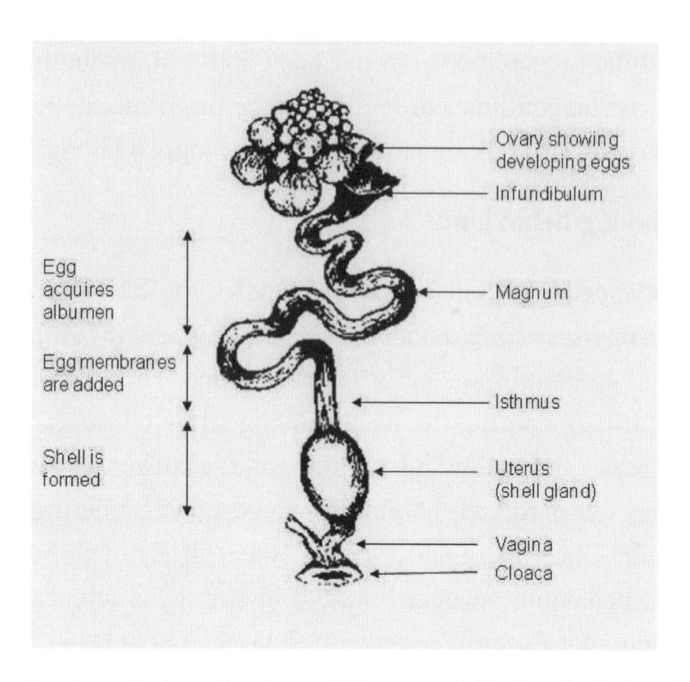

gland) where it stays for about 20 hours while the shell-forming glands get to work. Calcium which is the main constituent of the shell is released here. The shape and colour of the shell are also determined in the uterus. Finally the bloom or cuticle is added and the egg is laid with the small end coming out first. The bloom will be wet to the touch if you happen on an egg just laid, but quickly dries. In all, the egg has taken about 25 hours to form from ovulation to laying. The hen will stand to lay her egg – it is quite fascinating to watch this process if you happen to be there at the right time. In a regularly laying bird, an egg is laid about every 26 hours. So within an hour of one egg being laid the process starts again. In winter the time between eggs increases so the hybrids will lay about every 27 to 28 hours. Bantam eggs will invariably be small but some of the bigger bantams such as Wyandotte, Welsummer or Marans will lay a good sized egg and the yolk will be surprisingly large in comparison to the white.

Egg Production

A pure breed will lay 12 or so eggs – this is called a 'clutch' – and then she will have a 'pause' lasting several days and if she doesn't go broody (get the urge to sit on her eggs) will start laying another clutch. Hens usually have some time off laying while they are moulting in the autumn and will start laying again in January or February but probably only lay about half what they manage to lay at their peak. In January and February pure breeds tend to lay erratically, maybe every two or three days. In April and May they will be at their peak, laying every day with one day off a week. In August and September, hens will reduce the amount of eggs they are laying as the days shorten and then stop completely when they come in to moult. Hybrids will lay straight through their first winter but will moult their next autumn and should come back into lay after their moult. Eggs from pullets are usually quite small when they first start laying; they will gradually get bigger and will be at their biggest in the second year of laying.

Light plays a vital role in egg production. It affects a small organ behind the eye which in turn sends messages to the ovary and affects the ovulation process. So it is natural for a hen to lay in the spring and go out of lay in the shorter days of autumn. Professional eggs farmers overcome this problem by using artificial light and are therefore able to maintain the same amount of light every day which evens out the egg production.

You may find that your pullets or indeed two or three-year-old hens are reluctant to start laying in February. This is when you can start using layers pellets. You can feed layers mash or pellets in the morning and mixed poultry grain in the afternoon. Your best layers will be those who show a general sprightliness, being alert and active and who spend much of their day foraging and scratching for worms and other grubs in leaves or loose soil. They will be the ones who are first up and last to go to bed.

The Egg Itself

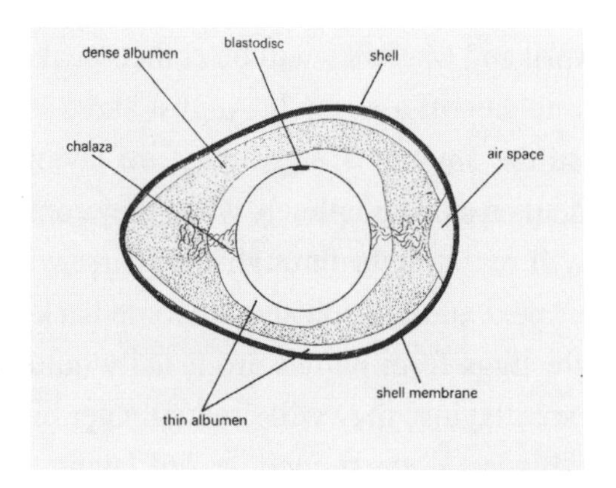

The egg is the age-old symbol of creation. Many ancient societies believed that the world was egg-shaped and was hatched from an egg made by God. The custom of presenting eggs is believed to have originated in Persia and was adopted by the Christians at Easter as a symbol of the resurrection of Christ, the eggs being coloured red in token of the blood of the redemption. The decoration of eggs for Easter is a traditional art in parts of Russia and Eastern European countries such as Romania. Eggs used to be dyed various colours using onion skins, logwood, furze flowers and other wild flowers and herbs.

Eggs are the supreme gift from hens to human beings – the perfect food impeccably packaged, full of protein. The egg is one of the most versatile ingredients used in many dishes, both savoury and sweet. The white or albumen is nearly 88% water, 10% protein, .05% fat typically and .82% ash. The yolk is 49% water, 16.7% protein, 32% fat and 1.9% ash.

Eggs should be stored in their boxes to avoid absorption of different flavours through the shells and with large end up to keep the air cell in place and the yolk centred. The air cell or bubble is a small space at the bottom rounded end of an egg. As an egg ages, this air space gets bigger. Many people store their eggs in the fridge but a better place for them is a cool room. In any case they need to be brought up to room temperature before being cooked. If you store your eggs in the fridge and try to boil them straight from the fridge the shells are likely to crack. Hard-boiled eggs will peel more easily if they are at least a week old; peeling under cold running water also helps. A cloudy white is a sign of freshness because of the high carbon dioxide content when the egg is laid. The carbon dioxide contained in the albumen leaks out through the porous shell as the egg ages. Factory processes prevent this by dipping the eggs in a special oil which seals the pores of the shell and this prevents loss of moisture. The other reasons your eggs should not be stored in the fridge is that bacteria can be absorbed through the porous shell more easily in the enclosed space. Also eggs kept at this lower temperature can cause the valuable protein to break down. I advise you not to keep eggs in the compartments located in the doors of fridges either because the opening and shutting of the door means eggs are not being kept at a constant temperature. And one final point: supermarkets do not keep their eggs in chilled cabinets because it is not the best place for them.

To tell if your eggs are fresh you can put them into a deep bowl of water. If they sink and lie on their side then they are fresh with a small air space. If they stand up and bob on the bottom then the air cell is larger and they aren't quite as fresh. If they float to the surface then they are bad with bacteria likely to have perforated the porous shell and to have caused the creation of gas. If you have an egg and can't recall whether it is raw or hard-boiled, spin it and then quickly stop it from spinning and let go. If it continues to spin again it is raw because the liquid inside is continuing to go round. If when you break an egg onto a plate or into a frying pan, the egg white is thick and doesn't spread and the yolk stands up then the egg is very fresh.

You can tell if an egg is fertile or not (a fertile egg is one where the cockerel has successfully mated with the egg layer) by looking at the yolk. An infertile egg will have a small, ragged white dot on one side of the yolk and this is called a blastodisc. On a fertile egg the white dot is larger with a more regular white circle; this is called a blastoderm.

The Egg-shell

The egg-shell is made up of calcium carbonate and protein and is porous (perforated all over with tiny holes) designed so that the developing chick can breathe. It is a remarkably complex structure consisting of several layers. Egg-shells can vary in colour from deep brown through to white with many shades of beige in between with or without a speckled effect. There are also the turquoise/green eggs laid by the Araucana.

The thickness of the egg-shell is determined by the amount of time it spends in the shell gland (uterus) – if the egg shell spends a short time in the uterus it will be thinner. The time of day also determines thickness – the earlier in the day that the egg-shell is formed the thicker it will be. The age of the hen can also affect the quality of the shell – as she grows older the shell can become thinner. The egg-shell acquires its colour or pigment in the final stages of its development in the oviduct and only in the outer layer of the egg-shell. The colour of the eggs laid by one hen can also vary; as she continues to lay, eggs which started off dark brown may fade to a lighter brown. Too much sun on the back of hen can cause lighter coloured egg-shells.

Egg-shells can sometimes become dirty if it is muddy outside and your hens get muddy feet. Some of this dirt can get on the egg. Also shells can be stained with chicken poop; this might be from the nest box but it is also possible that a little poop gets deposited on the egg as it is laid. Chickens excrete and lay eggs through the same opening (the Cloaca). Eggs are laid with a natural bloom over the porous shell to prevent bacteria being absorbed through it. If possible try and brush or wipe any dirt off the egg-shell with a paper towel. If you do need to wash dirty eggs then it is best to use hot water that is warmer than the egg; the contents of the egg will expand and push out any invading microbes. If you were to use cold water then it could cause bacteria on the surface of the shell to be drawn into the egg.

Selling your Eggs

You do not need to register as an egg producer in order to sell eggs to friends, neighbours or at your gate. You cannot supply them to a shop to sell unless you are registered. You should not describe them as 'free range' or 'organic' or size them as these are legal definitions.

PROBLEMS WITH EGGS

Shell-less Eggs

Soft-shelled or shell-less eggs with just the membrane around the egg can be quite a common problem especially with hybrids. This may happen in young pullets - the egg goes down through the oviduct so quickly that there is no time for the shell to be made. Sometimes the pullets are adjusting to their new egg-laying functions and the first few eggs will have no shell, but after a couple of weeks the eggs should be normal. If an egg has a very thin shell, your hen may not be getting enough calcium or vitamin D in her diet and you could try giving her crushed oyster shells and some cod liver oil in her feed. If your hen is still laying soft-shelled eggs after two or three weeks, it may be due to some inherent weakness in the strain which does not allow proper assimilation of calcium or an intrinsic malfunctioning of the reproductive tract - this could have been caused by infectious bronchitis or another disease when the hen was younger or intensive breeding may have led to malformed ovaries; in this case you may just decide to keep her as a pet. In my experience intensive egg layers such as ex-caged hens also sometimes have problems with soft-shelled eggs due to worn out reproductive systems. Some people say a sudden shock due to a low flying aeroplane can cause soft shells but I don't agree. All my hens are subjected to the same shocks but only the intensive layers produce the shell-less eggs.

Tiny Eggs

Occasionally your hen may lay a tiny egg which has no yolk. The egg may contain a fragment of tissue torn away from the ovary and as it passes down the oviduct it serves as a nucleus which stimulates the internal mechanism to operate and produce a tiny egg - it is known as a wind, cock or witch egg. This problem normally occurs in new pullets or in hens at the end of their laying season.

Double-yolked Eggs

Double yolks are sometimes produced by pullets in their first laying season. This is caused by two eggs separating from the ovary at the same time and joining into one egg.

Egg Eating

Shell-less eggs or eggs with thin shells in the nest box on a regular basis could lead to the abnormal behaviour of egg-eating. Once hens start eating eggs it can become a habit difficult to cure. One remedy would be to make the nest boxes as dark as possible so the hen cannot see the egg that she has laid and to collect your eggs more frequently. Also if you put lots of straw or hay in the nest boxes and a false egg there is a good chance the real egg will get buried as it is laid so that the guilty hen fails to find it and maybe takes a peck at the fake egg.

Egg Bound

If a hen seems to be constantly going to the nest box but laying no eggs and shows signs of distress, it may be assumed that she is egg bound. The egg may be too large and will have got stuck, even though it is ready to be laid. A little oil can be inserted gently into the vent as this may loosen the egg and allow it to be released. Another suggestion is to hold the bottom half of the hen carefully over steaming water for several minutes. This treatment generally relaxes and softens that part of the body, and the egg may then come out. If the egg breaks inside the hen it will probably kill her but she will also die if she cannot pass the egg.

Internal Egg Laying (Peritonitis)

In this condition egg yolks drop into the body cavity, instead of entering the oviduct. This can happen if a new layer is stressed at ovulation leading to the odd yolk being laid internally; but it may be that a hen with this problem has damaged her oviduct in which case she will continue to lay eggs internally. The yolks can be absorbed over time into her system and the hen might survive. The bird will have a swollen abdomen and may become lethargic and adopt an upright penguin-like stance. But sometimes several yolks may descend together which results in a build up and infection will set in; the resulting peritonitis can quickly become fatal. Antibiotics can help the infection but the internal egg laying cannot be cured; it is possible for the vet to spay your hen but this will not be cheap. An alternative is to have the hen put down.

Prolapse

Prolapse may occur as a result of straining to lay too large an egg or because a pullet starts laying eggs before its body is ready. The hen's bottom will look lower than usual because the vent muscles are pushed out. You will see a bulge which is a red mass of tissue pushing out through the vent. The area can be bathed or some Vaseline applied and then the tissue needs to be firmly pressed back in with a warm piece of flannel.

Blood or Meat Spots and Rings

You may see a small blood spot or ring at the edge of the yolk or a meat spot in the white when you break one of your hens' eggs. These are completely harmless. They are caused by the rupture of a blood vessel in the ovary which may have occurred due to a sudden fright.

COCKERELS

A cockerel is not needed for hens to lay eggs but will be needed to produce fertile eggs in order to hatch chicks. Cockerels can disturb neighbours by crowing in the night and at dawn but do have some advantages. They can prove surprisingly thoughtful when looking after the hens on their patch, often calling them over to enjoy tasty morsels. They usually do most of their mating between April and October. Young fertile cockerels generally have a red tinge showing on their legs. A cockerel will approach a hen and stand erect in front of her with his neck feathers ruffled. He will then dance around her with the wing nearest her spread downwards. The hen, if a willing one, will duck down and allow him to mount her. He will use his wings to maintain his balance and grip her by the nape of her neck while he mates (hens may lose some feathers on top of their heads as a result). The cockerel may also be quite cunning, luring his hens over by calling them to food and then jumping on them! I have noticed that my cockerels very sensibly choose to mate with hens that are laying. Cockerels become much less fertile with age; one that is over four or five should not be relied on.

The problems with mating occur with the high-ranking hens who reject the cockerel's attentions by flying off and refusing to let him near them. Research has been carried out on cockerels and their reproductive abilities. Cockerels will apparently produce more sperm if a new hen comes on the scene. They will also devote more sperm to their first mating with a new hen. An attractive hen with a large comb will receive more sperm than a less attractive female. These large-combed hens will also tend to be reproductively superior producing more eggs with bigger yolks.

Dealing with Aggressive Cockerels

Young cockerels and pullets are equal in the pecking order until the cockerel matures. Cockerels in general can be aggressive towards other hens and certainly have their favourites. It is normal for a cockerel to look after up to 12 hens and he can easily keep this number fertile. Cockerels who only have a few hens to look after can wear the females out with their attentions. They can be aggressive towards each other and too many cockerels will create problems as they will spend more time fighting than looking after the flock. Bantam cockerels are often more aggressive than their large fowl counterparts. If a cockerel becomes aggressive with you there are a couple of tips for sorting him out. Your cockerel is feeling threatened and trying hard to protect his flock of hens. You need to prove who is master. Wear a pair of good gardening gloves and pick him up. Carry him around with you whilst you carry out normal chores with your hens. When you have done this several times he should be much calmer and will hopefully realise you are not a danger to his hens and that you are boss. Another idea is to press your hand down hard on his back, making him squat - again you are showing him you are in charge.

Crowing

The cockerel's crowing at dawn was deemed very important by the ancients. Soldiers would change watch timed by it. The Roman writer, Pliny claimed that 'sluggish men would never rise from their beds with the exhortations of the crested bird.' Cockerels were also valued as weather forecasters, predicting rain with their raucous crowing and flapping of wings. It was believed that when the cock crowed at dawn all ghosts and evil spirits would return to the underworld.

Cock-crowing competitions used to take place in the US in the early 1900s as well as across Europe and Russia where the Yurlov Crower was bred specifically for competitions. In these competitions a time-keeper would note down the duration of each contestant's crow and the number of crows in a given length of time, usually up to 30 minutes. In Germany there is a breed called Bergse Kraaier which has a reputation for having the longest and loudest crow. In the US today there are still cock crowing competitions.

In the last few years cock-crowing has proved a sensitive issue between chicken keepers and their neighbours - several cases have been either brought to court or settled by the Local Council. If complaints are received the Council are obliged to investigate. Environmental Services Officers will consider: the source of noise, environment of the noise, duration of crowing, time of day and how often the cockerel crows. Practical measures will be suggested such as moving the said cockerel as far away from neighbouring properties as possible; keeping the housing dark and even lowering the ceiling so that the cockerel is prevented from throwing his head back to crow. Competition between other cockerels in the area can also be a problem. People are always searching for ways of silencing crowing. In the US cockerels can be taken to the vet and have their vocal chords removed; in Britain this is not allowed. Making a hen house sound proof is impossible because birds need ventilation. One method that has been used is to put a bar across the roof loosely so that it swings when the cockerel's head touches it, as he throws his head back. But a canny cockerel would just jump down from his perch to crow standing on the floor.

Trimming Spurs

Spurs are continually growing and like toe nails they may need to be trimmed. This can be done with dog nail clippers. You must be careful only to clip back the tip which is the dead tissue but you don't want to cut too far or you will get some bleeding as spurs have a blood supply in the core (you will be able to see the blood vessels under light). As a rough guide, on most adult cockerels this will be about 1½ to 2cm from the base of the spur so you need to leave this part intact.

GENERAL HEALTH

My hybrids will live up to five or six but my rescue hens, which are ex-caged birds, only live around four years if very lucky (as constant egg laying will wear them out). Pure breeds tend to live longer, usually seven or eight years but cross breeds will live the longest in my experience. We had an Araucana cross who lived until she was 10 years old and then went downhill gradually until she died of natural causes. Sometimes a hen will die while still young, for no apparent reason and with few symptoms showing. Be aware that not all vets will treat sick hens and the treatments offered – eg antibiotics – may not be successful in curing your hen. In general a laying hen is a healthy hen. The younger hens who have just started laying, tend to be the ones first up in the morning, with much of their day spent actively foraging and they will also be the last to bed.

Moulting and Feather Loss

All hens moult once a year usually in the autumn but do not moult in their first year of laying. They will stop laying while they moult; feathers are full of protein and all the hen's energies and protein that she produces will go into growing her new set of feathers. She will lose her feathers in a sequence; this means she will never be entirely without plumage. The first feathers to go will be on the head and neck, followed by some on the saddle, then the breast and abdomen, then wing feathers will drop but not all at once so the ability to fly will not be totally lost. All the primary flight feathers will gradually be replaced. The last to disappear will be the tail feathers.

The moulting process usually takes between six to eight weeks. Good layers and hybrids may come back into lay after the moult for the winter period. Others including many of the pure breeds will not start laying again until early spring. While hens are in moult they tend to lose bits of scaly skin which you will find on the hen house floor along with the feathers. This is quite natural. Chickens will also change the scales on their legs and feet once a year. Poor layers tend to go into moult rather early in late summer while the best layers will moult late, probably in November. It is not so well known but pullets or young hens also lose feathers and can have up to four changes of feathers by the time they are 28 weeks old. Although cockerels are meant to moult in a similar way to hens I often find that my cockerels don't become nearly as bare; I think the feathers are being replaced so gradually that it is almost imperceptible. Some cockerels lose only a few feathers at a time and since they have a lot of feathers, one barely notices the body and wing feathers being renewed. The tail feathers are such a noticeable feature that a cockerel with no tail really stands out and can look very odd. You may notice that his neck becomes scraggy when he moults in this area. But in general cockerels don't seem to drop nearly as many feathers as hens.

Chickens in the Heat

Chickens find it more difficult to cope in the heat than in the cold. They will hold their wings away from their bodies to increase their surface area and try to dissipate the heat. They will also gasp and keep their beaks open. Be sure to provide plenty of sheltered areas. The optimum temperature for a hen is 21°C (this is the sort of temperature her ancestors would have enjoyed on the jungle floor!) but of course chickens in Britain are not going to experience these temperatures all year round.

Hens in Cold Winters

Certainly the recent cold winters have made it hard for chickens to cope. I found that my younger hens were absolutely fine but older stock and any hens that went into a late moult have found it quite difficult. Extra feed will help keep them warm; oats will be welcome and also the maize that comes with mixed poultry grain will help. A bird's feathers are a wonderful insulator and when roosting their feet are covered by feathers so keep reasonably warm. Frozen water in the drinkers is a problem and I have to knock ice out of containers and refill them several times a day in the really snowy weather. Bringing drinkers in for the night to defrost and putting them out again in the morning is not a bad idea. Be aware that plastic containers become very brittle and are easily broken in freezing weather. Galvanized metal drinkers, though, are a nightmare when water becomes frozen solid inside them.

Any hens or cockerels with large combs and wattles may be at risk of frostbite in particularly cold periods. In order to prevent it you can rub Vaseline into the comb and the wattles.

PROBLEMS, PARASITES AND DISEASES

Aspergillosis

This is a type of pneumonia which may break out in chicks. It involves a species of fungus found in mouldy litter or stale food. Birds affected will appear unsteady on their feet and will be gasping and breathing heavily. There is no cure and infected chicks should be humanely killed.

Bumblefoot

Bumblefoot is a condition that affects the pads of a bird's feet. It is a bacterial infection and can occur if perches are too high off the ground and the bird damages her pads as she flies down. There will be a swelling on the foot and there may be a dark, blackish scab. The swelling is due to an abscess in the pad; you can try soaking the infected foot and see if you can squeeze out the pus. In any case she will probably need antibiotics which will mean a trip to the vets.

Coccidiosis

This disease is caused by the Coccidia parasite. Symptoms will include listlessness with head sunk into the neck, white diarrhoea and sometimes blood in the droppings. Treat with Proleth in the drinking water.

Colds

The common cold can affect your hens and is often due to bad ventilation or cold conditions. There will be discharge from the nostrils and sneezing. Isolate the birds affected and sponge their faces gently with warm water and dose with a little cod liver oil.

Crop Bound (Impacted Crop)

Hens only have a small gizzard for grinding up their food – this is quite a long process as they have no teeth to chew anything up. The food that has been stored in the crop will, during the night, gradually go down into the gizzard and the crop will be pretty much empty by the morning. If a hen is crop bound it will feel hard and even hang down heavily. If the hen is picked up a hard ball of food which has accumulated will be felt – often this is a twisted ball of grass which is then too large to pass down. A lubricant such as a little olive oil can be poured down her throat – this is easiest done with a syringe - and if the crop is gently massaged, the food should soften and pass through. Liquid paraffin can be used as an alternative (olive oil can be bad for the chicken's liver) – apparently liquid paraffin does not go through the liver but passes out with the droppings. Alternatively the hen can be given a drink of warm water, then turned upside down and the crop gently massaged to try and release the blockage. The hen can be fed some soft food in the interim. If the impaction does not clear then the best option is to consult a vet – he may make a small incision in her breast and be able to remove the blockage. **Sour Crop** is a yeast infection that leads to a thickening of the crop wall and dilation and is caused by an overgrowth of Candida (fungal species). An infected hen will be out of sorts and have bad breath. Mouldy food can be a cause. There is no specific treatment but a prebiotic (Beryl's Friendly Bacteria) may help restore natural bacteria.

Depluming Mite

The depluming mite is a burrowing mite related to the scaly leg mite. It burrows into the feather shafts particularly on the head, neck and back. Damage to the tissue causes it to ooze a fluid which the mite feed on. The hen will lose weight and lay fewer eggs. The mite are transmitted from bird to bird via direct contact. Invermectin 1% is used to treat these mite but is only available through a vet.

Feather Pecking

Feather pecking between hens can be a real problem and is especially common if hens are confined in a small space and become bored. It is also thought feather pecking can occur because something is lacking in their diet – feathers are full of protein. Severe feather pecking, characterised by forceful pecks and pulling whole feathers out is much worse since the bullied hen may develop bald patches that are at the mercy of more pecking and puncturing of the skin; unfortunately hens like blood and would eat the flesh of another chicken (which is rich in amino acids) and once wounds develop things can only go from bad to worse. There are anti feather pecking sprays available to use on affected bare areas that will put the culprits off pecking out more feathers. You could also try Gentian violet spray which turns any red patches purple (chickens are attracted to the red but not purple); or you could use iodine which is an antiseptic wound cleaner and will put birds off pecking as well.

If the pecking gets worse you will need to isolate the affected bird and allow any wounds to heal. Treating with Stockholm tar is an old fashioned remedy which can be applied to any wounds and will stop feather pecking. The feathers won't regrow while a hen is in constant egg production and it may not be until moulting in the autumn that a hen will replace lost feathers. Another reason for loss of feathers is the over vigorous attentions of a cockerel – often feathers are lost just behind the comb on top of the head where the cockerel grabs his hen in order not to lose his balance. Feathers on her back may also be lost as he straddles her – saddles can be bought and fixed onto the hen's back to protect her.

Fleas

Poultry fleas usually settle clustered like brown spots around the head and sometimes cause bare patches in the feathers. Treat birds with flea powder and treat the hen house as well in order to get rid of flea eggs.

Fowl Pox

This is a virus that can affect chickens and is similar to chicken pox in humans. It spreads either from a wound on an affected bird to an open wound on another bird or biting insects can carry the infection or it may be transferred by air from pox infected mammals. There are two types, wet (diphtheritic) and dry (cutaneous). In the dry form raised crusted areas form on the featherless areas such as the comb, wattles and around the eyes. These eventually form black scabs. With the wet form, which is rarer, ulcer-like lumps form in the mouth and wind pipe and this is more dangerous because affected birds may have trouble breathing. There is no specific treatment, although vets will usually prescribe antibiotics to prevent secondary bacteria if a bird is infected with wet fowl pox. There is no vaccine currently licensed in the UK to prevent this disease.

Heart Disease

This will be evident in old chickens and the most obvious sign will be a purple comb and loss of energy.

Infectious Bronchitis

The symptoms for bronchitis are similar to that of a cold. There will also be a decrease in egg production and the oviduct will be permanently damaged resulting in a future of soft-shelled eggs.

Lice (fleas)

These are irritating for the bird and can be treated by dousing the birds with louse powder. You can also dust the nest boxes and dust baths with the powder. Broody hens should be dusted with powder before sitting on their eggs.

Marek's Disease

This is a common virus that causes tumours – clinical signs include paralysis of legs, wings and neck; loss of weight; grey iris or irregular pupil; vision impairment; and the skin around feather follicles can be raised and roughened. The disease was first recognised by the Hungarian vet Jozsef Marek in 1907 and was at one time the most common cause of losses in the poultry industry though now largely controlled by the use of vaccines. It usually affects birds between five and 25 weeks of age. It is a highly contagious disease that may survive for months or years in litter and poultry dust. Infection occurs through the respiratory tract and infected birds can remain carriers long after infection. There is no treatment.

Mycoplasma

This is a respiratory infection which starts with sneezing and coughing, a runny nose and eyes, and sometimes a rasping noise in the affected bird's breathing can be heard. Other symptoms can be swollen eyes and gasping for breath; you will see your hen raise her head and open her beak wide to try and gain extra air into her lungs. Unfortunately mycoplasma can spread quickly through a flock; birds with good immune systems will avoid it but the more susceptible young or old hens may go down with a bout. New hens arriving to join a flock will be especially vulnerable since they are also undergoing the stress of moving. Mycoplasma can be treated with an antibiotic (such as Tylan 200) but you will need to take your hen to the vet as this will be injected straight into her breast. You can also get a prescription for Tylan 200 in the form of antibiotic powder which you add to the drinking water at a ratio of 0.5g to a litre of water.

Newcastle Disease

This is a notifiable disease and is highly contagious caused by the paramyxo virus with the last outbreak in 1997. Symptoms include loss of appetite, coughing, diarrhoea and paralysis or twisted neck.

Northern Fowl Mite

This mite is similar to red mite but is found on the birds during the day. The mite lay their eggs at the base of feathers around the vent. Large number can cause a hen to become anaemic. Treat with mite powder containing diatoms.

Red Mite

Red mite are carried by wild birds and live and breed in crevices of the hen house. At night they run along the perches and up the chicken's leg where they suck blood from its flesh. They don't live on the bird but can be spotted during the day – they will be red if they have recently sucked blood, otherwise they will be grey. An indication that red mite are present is a greyish powder at the ends of the perches or in corners of the hen houses. If you wipe perches clean with paper towel you will know for certain that you have red mite if you find red streaks on the towel. Affected chickens will become anaemic and look jaundiced through losing blood and you may see tiny blood spots on their eggs; affected hens may eventually stop laying. If you have roofing felt on your hen house then at some point you are likely to get red mite. They will reside under the roofing felt and the only way to get rid of them will be to remove the felt completely. Nowadays many hen houses are made using corrugated Onduline for the roofs as this is made of bituminous material and is less prone to harbouring red mite.

If you get an infestation it is not always easy to eradicate red mite rapidly. There are sprays available to kill them; some may work for a while and then the red mite will be back. Poultry

Shield or Smite can be tried. Dismantling the hutch and using a blow torch on bad areas of red mite can work quite well and a pressure washer will get rid of most of the mite. Other possibilities include ant powder or smearing bad patches with a mixture of paraffin and Vaseline. One of the most effective ways of dealing with red mite is to use diatoms (diatomaceous earth). Diatoms are the fossilised remains of micro skeletons which are a type of algae. You sprinkle the powder at the end of perches and crevices and the microscopically sharp edges pierce the out waxy coatings of the mite which will cause them to dry up and die.

Scaly Leg Mite

The scaly leg mite lives under the scales of the bird's leg. It is contagious and can be seen in birds of all ages. It may originate from the litter on the floor of your hen house. The scales on the legs become rough, and a chalk-like concretion is formed, which accumulates both between and over the scales. It is intensely irritating to the bird and once the mite take hold may make the bird lame and unable to perch. The problem is relatively easy to cure and there are several different treatments that can be tried. Surgical spirit can be painted on the legs with a small paintbrush once a week for five weeks and is usually effective. Other treatments include scaly cream which is available in pet shops (used for budgies with scaly face); Eucalyptus oil which is an organic treatment and must be rubbed into the legs every few weeks; the legs can be scrubbed with paraffin (an old fashioned remedy) using an old toothbrush (one treatment should be enough); dipping the legs in linseed oil, which reduces the irritation, softens the scales and promotes healing but you need to repeat this treatment; Vaseline or petroleum jelly gently rubbed into the legs can help. You may kill the mite but the scales may not recover until the yearly moult.

Worms

There are six different types of worms which can live in the internal parts of chickens. Roundworms (ascarids) are probably the most common. They produce eggs which are laid in the intestines and pass out through the faeces. Then they may be picked up by the hens, hatch in the intestine and you may see long thin cylindrical worms in the droppings, which can be up to 12cm long; these are more likely to be seen once treatment has taken effect. The other less common worms are two types of capillary or thread worms which occur in the oesophagus and crop and a relatively harmless caecal worm which lives in the caeca or guts. Tapeworms are relatively common but are harmless and untreatable. Chickens get infected by eating snails, slugs and other insects. Eggs hatch in the intestinal wall and the worms can be seen in the droppings. They are flattened, ribbon-shaped with several segments and can be a few centimetres long.

Symptoms in bad cases of the common roundworms include anaemic looking comb and wattles, loss of weight resulting in a razor sharp breast bone, listlessness, permanently mucky bottom and a reduction in eggs. You should treat for worms with Flubenvet (flubendazole) – this is available from feed suppliers or online. It comes in 60g pots which is enough to treat up to 20 birds over the required seven consecutive days; it is a white powder and should be mixed into the feed (the correct does is 3g to 1kg of feed). You can mix it up in a bucket and use a little vegetable oil to help the powder stick to the grain/pellets. If you have only a few hens, cut a grape in half and add a pinch of powder inside and feed one to each hen. You do not need to stop eating the eggs while treating with Flubenvet.

A particularly nasty worm is the gape worm which lives in the lungs and trachea of the bird. An affected hen can't breathe properly and gasps for air as her airway is obstructed by the worms. This can prove fatal unless treated immediately – a vet may prescribe Panacur which is administered orally and while treatment is ongoing, eggs must be discarded.

On the subject of worming in general, some authorities say that you should treat for worms twice a year whether your hens show symptoms or not and some say that de-worming a healthy hen weakens the system and upsets the natural balance of helpful organisms. I think that birds that are confined all the time should be wormed regularly but that free range hens are less susceptible and therefore worming is less essential. There are also herbal remedies such as VermX but I cannot swear to its effectiveness.

PREDATORS

Foxes are the most common and dangerous killers of hens as I am sure you all know, and usually strike early in the morning or at dusk, although in urban areas foxes seem to be seen more and more active during the day. One often hears stories of foxes killing all the hens a family owns in one go. People wonder why a fox has to kill every hen in sight and only carry off one or two. He only does this because he has been disturbed; left to his own devices he would come back and carry off each carcass to bury as food for the future. He is an opportunist and cleverer than we suppose. To protect their hens, many people use electric fencing, which seems to prove effective – once the fox has experienced an electric shock he is unlikely to come back. Otherwise you need high fencing (at least 2m) with wire dug 30cm into the ground and an overhang of wire at the top so that the fox will find it too difficult to climb over. If hens are free-ranging and you live in the country you are not so likely to get foxes visiting during the day. However I have lost hens who have roosted in the tree and come down at 5am in the morning in the summer when foxes are still about. Foxes can be trapped but in my experience they are too wily and avoid entering the traps. If you live in the countryside, foxes can multiply fairly quickly and may need to be controlled. The best solution is to get hold of a gamekeeper to shoot them.

Other preventative ideas are sprinkling human urine around runs as foxes hate human smells or tying up stockings filled with human hair. Last summer I also used a radio, setting it to Radio 4 at dusk and left it on outside through the night; the sound of human voices was effective at keeping the fox away. And one final option which is only possible if you have an acre of land: you could get a couple of alpacas (castrated males are meant to be the most vigilant). They have been known to deter foxes, and even attack those that enter their field.

Badgers operating at night will kill and eat any hen that is susceptible – i.e. sitting on eggs in a secret location. Badgers can easily burrow under normal fences and break their way into hen houses through any weak spots as they are strong and determined. They can also lift vertical pop hopes with their snout and undo easy latches. Bolts however will defeat them. Unlike foxes who will kill a whole flock, the badger will only kill one hen per night and eat most of the carcass on the spot. Unfortunately badgers are protected by law so you cannot easily get rid of a badger. In my case I had a badger problem over a period of four years. Every so often he/she would come at night killing and eating a vulnerable hen. Not so long ago one and same badger arrived in the hens' stable one morning and I found it curled up in some straw. I had to call in the RSPCA to take it away. It was taken to a Wildlife Hospital and put down as its teeth were worn out with age.

Many breeds of dogs, used to killing game, can also be a major danger to hens, easily decimating small flocks. If a neighbour's dog kills hens on private land then a case may be brought against the owners. If hens are wandering onto public land then it is a different matter. Dogs can of course be trained to leave hens well alone. Cats can and do kill chicks.

Rats can kill chicks and eat eggs as can magpies. Sparrow hawks and buzzards may swoop down and take chicks and small bantams. If you live near a river you may have a problem with mink which like to kill and eat chickens. Weasels and stoats, despite being so small, if they can get into a hen house, can bite sleeping chickens in the neck and kill them.

Rats and mice can also become a big problem if food is left lying around. The chicken droppings may also attract the rats. Mice will gnaw their way into sacks of corn if left out of lidded dustbins.

FITTING THE GARDENING IN AROUND YOUR HENS

I grow herbs, vegetables, fruit and flowers alongside my hens. Vegetable-growing works well with hens. Think back to the Second World War when many families grew their own veg and kept their own chickens successfully. Nothing goes to waste as you can always feed surplus vegetables to the chickens. First you must plan where you are going to grow your vegetables and how you will protect seedlings and young plants from your hens. You will need to protect some of your vegetables if your hens are free ranging.

Netting is an option or building a vegetable cage. Low fences are also an idea – you can get rolls of green, sturdy chicken wire which are 60cm high – hens don't usually fly over these; they tend to fly onto fences such as post and rails because they can perch on the rails on their way over but they find it difficult to perch on chicken wire! Alternatively you can buy or make raised vegetable boxes, use tunnels, cloches, containers or invest in hanging baskets. Some people mulch around precious plants and seedlings with rough gravel, use crinkly lawn edging or surround with twiggy sticks – all should prevent scratching feet. Another idea is to use a clipped edging of box or rosemary but this would, obviously, take some time to develop.

To a large extent what hens will eat in your garden depends on how much access to grassy areas they have. The more land they have to free range, the more likely they are to feast on weeds, wild herbs and grass; it follows therefore that they are less likely to eat your precious plants, flowers and herbs. I can't stress enough how important grass is – I bought a couple of 20 week old hybrids recently who had been kept inside a barn. I put them in a run with grass and they went crazy for it, pecking at the grass ferociously as though it was going to be taken away at any moment. If your hens have only a little space to roam around and a small area of grass and greenery they will very soon have eaten all the grass and anything else that is green. It follows that if you keep your hens enclosed and let them out to free range every so often they will eat anything that's green including vegetables, herbs, weeds, beech hedges and some of your flowers! Your hens shouldn't touch snowdrops, crocuses, primroses, violas, buttercups, daffodils or tulips. Other flowers they shouldn't be interested in include lavender, roses, asters, camellias, dahlias, azaleas, hydrangeas, chrysanthemums, and irises. Most evergreen shrub and bushes especially prickly ones are unlikely to be eaten.

Strong smelling herbs such as rosemary, mint, sage, thyme and feverfew are not attractive. Mine don't eat the parsley or chives but I know of some hens that do. On the vegetable front your hens shouldn't touch carrots, parsnips, leeks, potatoes, squashes and pumpkins. Climbing beans should be fine once established as they won't be able to reach most of the beans (you need to protect seedlings, maybe using a cold frame). Hens love eating surplus sweet corn. You could also think about growing some sunflowers and feed them the seeds. Spinach, chard, kale, broccoli, cabbage and lettuce (except for the spicy oriental leaves) will be popular; beetroot leaves are particularly relished and my hens also eat beetroot and courgettes if cut in half and love Jerusalem artichokes which I let them nibble on when I have a surplus in the winter months. They shouldn't eat the leaves so a good vegetable to cultivate when you have hens. My hens don't usually eat spring onions but just recently teenage chicks have been tucking into the green stems of my onions!

On the berry front, hens love strawberries, raspberries and all edible berries except blackcurrants which are too sour. Plants that hens love include weeds such as chickweed (named because chicks loved it). Your hens will also eat dandelion, comfrey, sorrel, horseradish and dock leaves. Perennial geraniums, hollyhocks, nasturtiums and their seeds, busy lizzies, lobelia, pansies and hostas are all said to be popular. My chickens eat elderberries with no ill effects although these are said to be toxic. Tomato and potato leaves are thought to be toxic but chickens do occasionally nibble at these. Interestingly we have a beech hedge in the garden which the hens do not touch; however I have noticed a neighbour's hens, which are enclosed with no grass, have stripped all the leaves off the beech hedge as far up as they can reach. Other flowers that chickens will tuck into include marigolds (the petals will make their yolks even yellower); violets, border pinks and sweet peas – I would be surprised if any of these lasted for long! There are always exceptions to what hens will and won't eat – like us, different hens have different eating preferences.

Some hens eat lavender and even artichoke leaves which mine have never touched. On the whole hens will eat anything that tastes similar to grass. Unfortunately they won't eat nettles, (although I have read that some hens do eat wilted ones), bindweed, plantain, moss, ground elder, mallow or anything that is too bitter. Some hens will eat cleavers and groundsel but mine don't seem to.

Your hens will be a useful addition to the garden – they are very good at breaking up the soil after you have dug over your vegetable garden in the winter; they forage for pests and produce droppings, an excellent fertiliser. You should also allocate a patch of bare earth where your hens can enjoy their dust baths – hens clean themselves by flicking dry soil into their feathers and this helps keep them free from parasites. Chickens love to perch during the day either on a fence, low branch or on top of their hen house. They especially like to do this when the ground is wet.

Possible problems that might occur with your companion hens:

They may dig up newly planted seedlings

Your hens will make craters in areas of bare earth

Your hens will find their way through gaps in fences and holes in netting to get to juicy green vegetables

You will have to clean up chicken poop off paths and patios!

Hens love scratching in leaves in the autumn – if you rake your leaves into piles, beware of hens scattering them all over the garden again.

Poultry Manure and its Uses

Your hens will excrete between 25 and 50 times a day and do this while roosting as well. One hen produces about 5½kg of manure a year. It means you will end up with a lot of chicken poop – you may want to gather up poop from your lawn and put it straight in the compost bin which will also be filled with the manure and straw or wood shavings when you clean out the hutch or hutches. Poultry manure is an extremely valuable fertiliser. When added to the compost heap it will act as an activator as it is full of nitrogen. Fresh poultry manure is generally regarded as too strong to go straight onto vegetable plots, as it is full of ammonia and would burn the plants. It can be applied directly to comfrey. It can also be put around blackcurrant bushes as they love nitrogen. Droppings in a water butt produce excellent liquid feed. Moisture content is about 60% and this is why it needs to be dried. It also contains too much nitrogen so in order to use it as a complete manure, bone meal and potash need to be added. To every 12kg of manure, 3kg of bone meal and 150g of sulphate of potash need to be added. An alternative would be to use the dried poultry manure as a nitrogenous fertiliser and apply along rows of brassicas that need extra nitrogen. A good way of using poultry manure is to dry the droppings as quickly as possible spreading them out on metal trays in a shed and then pulverizing them possibly with the back of a spade. Poultry manure can also be effective with just potash added (bonfire ash from a wood fire is ideal).

BROODY HENS AND HATCHING CHICKS

Hens that Go Broody

Hens naturally go broody (i.e. want to sit on eggs) after they have laid between 12 and 20 eggs; they are more likely to turn broody if their eggs are left in their nests. Each hen warms her eggs every time she sits to lay an egg and sits longer as the time for broodiness approaches. Collecting the eggs every day prevents a hen going broody as easily. Breeds that make reliable broodies are Silkies, Gold Tops (Silkie/Light Sussex bantam cross), the little Pekins and the heavier breeds such as Orpingtons, Cochins, Brahmas or Maranses. Wyandottes also tend to go broody quite frequently and make good mothers. Hens may become broody two or three times in the spring and summer but not all hens have a tendency to broodiness. Hybrids have been bred specifically not to go broody and there are certain pure light breeds which are classified as non-sitters; these include Leghorn, Appenzeller, Vorwerk and Ancona. The exception to this rule are Araucanas, the blue egg layers who love to go broody.

Signs that a Hen is Broody

Classic symptoms of a broody hen are: firmly sitting in the nest box, reluctant to move and staying put overnight, fluffing up her feathers, clucking and trying to peck anyone lifting her off as she doesn't like her eggs interfered with. She may also have plucked feathers from her breast and inner legs to feather

her nest and allow her eggs to get closer to her warm body. When out of the nest box she will walk around, puffed up, clucking and behaving in a bad tempered way. She will eat and drink and then try to get back to her nest. If another hen sits on her nest or she is shut out she will sit outside on the bare ground, picking up twigs and straw and throwing them over her back, often enduring pecks from other hens.

Curing a Broody Hen

To stop a hen being broody, she should be put in an airy coop with a slatted or wire mesh floor where there is no opportunity for nesting. Ideally this coop should be raised off the ground as the air circulating around will lower her body temperature and stop her feeling broody. She should be given food and water and left for two or three days. If she still goes back to her nest when let out then put her back for another spell of solitary confinement. Other old fashioned remedies include dunking her in cold water or putting ice cubes under her (both rather unpleasant for the hen and not recommended!)

Fertile Eggs

If you have a cockerel, then as long as he is mating with your hens you should have plenty of fertile eggs. Under normal circumstances you will have collected your eggs daily. Then one of your hens becomes broody and stays in her nest box. Now you need to decide on a number of eggs and put them gently under your hen at the same time. Intended fertile eggs can be kept for up to ten days, stored on their side or on end but should be turned every day to stop the yolk adhering to the inner egg membrane. Eggs should be clean (dirty eggs can be washed in warm water) and should have good thick shells. An average sized hen can sit on between nine and 12 eggs (too many eggs may result in the outer ones getting chilled). If you buy in some fertile eggs either from a poultry farm or over the internet (ebay is a popular source) there is always a risk that the eggs may not be fertile or that some may fail. I had several failures last year with no eggs hatching. You should make sure the parents of any fertile eggs are not related as chicks hatched will be inbred and may have deformities, such as misshapen beaks or toes. If eggs are coming through the post, allow them to rest for 24 hours before setting under a hen. And lastly be aware that not all hens make good broodies; they sometimes abandon their eggs half way through the process so best to use 'tried and tested' broody hens if you can. You can test your broody hen by placing a couple of china eggs under her for a couple of days to make sure she is sitting well, before you put your fertile eggs under her.

Making a Safe Nest for your Hen

If you want to give her the best conditions then you can prepare a nest for your broody hen. You should use a box. and place a turf with the grass uppermost inside. If you turn the turf over and hollow out some of the earth this will create a dip. It is important that the nest is on turf as this allows natural moisture to come up from the earth. If the weather is very dry while your hen is sitting you can pour some warm water on the outer rim of the turf to keep it moist. Using hay or straw, make the nest circular but not too hollow or eggs will roll together and crack or too shallow so that the eggs roll out. The nest box should be put inside a hutch and attached to a wire run. You may have a hen who has gone broody in an unsuitable spot (she could be vulnerable to predators). Brooding is quite a secretive process for a hen and she will have chosen the darkest corner that she can find. If she is allowed to free range this could mean she has made a nest hidden away in the undergrowth in the corner of a garden, where she may have laid a substantial number of eggs. She and her eggs may need to be moved to your home-made safe nesting box. Also if your hen has gone broody in one of your main nest boxes you will need to move her and her eggs as you don't want other hens muscling in and laying additional eggs in her nest. This can be tricky; she may not be happy and may return to the old nest – it is best done at dusk and she should be watched the next day, when she comes off her nest to feed and drink, to make sure she returns to her new nest.

The Broody Process

Your sitting hen will automatically make her own storage conditions. She will have plucked feathers from her breast to line her nest. She will turn her eggs every day, keep them moist and come off for 20 or so minutes to feed, drink, poop and often have a quick dust bath. Eggs need to cool for a short time every day; this allows fresh air into them. You should check the eggs when she comes off and make sure none have broken or become soiled (dirty eggs can be washed in hot water and put back). If she is not coming off her eggs, you may gently need to lift her up and take her to food and water.

If by any chance your hen is late returning to her eggs, do not despair, they will probably still be okay. Your broody hen should be fed on mixed poultry corn during the time that she is sitting. When she goes back to her nest she will rearrange her eggs and turn them with her beak. This can happen up to 50 times a day and stops the yolk sticking to the side of the shell as it develops and also prevents the germ at the upper surface of the egg sticking to the shell membrane which would result in the death of the embryo. A small amount of grease from her body is transferred on to the eggs and this helps prevent the loss of moisture during storage. Also, if she is sitting on earth, this helps to produce humidity. Moisture, heat and oxygen are the essential conditions for successful hatching. The turning also helps to diffuse the oxygen which is conducted through the albumen to the embryo. When a hen is broody the normal warmth of her body is increased by the condition of the blood-vessels in that part of her body (mainly the breast from which she has plucked feathers) coming into contact with the eggs. These become distended and the accelerated blood flow causes the temperature of the atmosphere around the eggs to rise to about 39°C.

Candling

This was originally done by holding the egg up to the light of a candle to check on embryo growth. Nowadays a candler with a light bulb attached can be bought. This is basically a concentrated source of light so that one can see through the shell and check the development of a chick. You can also make your own candler – all you need is a cardboard box (cereal box works well). Make a round hole in one end which is roughly the diameter of an egg. Put a torch inside the box so that the light shines through the hole. Go into a dark room with your egg and place it over the hole. This can be done on the sixth or seventh day and on the seventeenth day and allows eggs to be discarded when the embryo has not developed. On the seventh day, if the egg is fertile, a dark shadow will be seen with veins running through it – it looks similar to a spider with red legs. An infertile egg is clear and shows the light clearly through it. On the seventeenth day fertile eggs will show a dense black mass with a clearly defined air cell at the broad end. This all works well on white and light brown eggs but it is not so easy to see development through dark brown eggs.

The Chicks Hatch

After 20 days for bantams or 21 days for large fowl, chicks will begin to emerge from their shells. Cheeping will be heard coming from inside the shell about 24 hours before the eggs are due to hatch and this will trigger the mother hen's maternal instincts. Shortly before hatching, the chicks take in the yolk sac via the umbilical cord which then closes up. The chick will then raise its head and the egg tooth on top of the beak will press a hole in the shell, causing the egg to crack open and the chick to hatch. While her chicks are hatching, Mother Hen will sit for approximately 48 hours and manage without food or water. She should be left alone for this period. Chicks do not need anything to eat for at least the first 24 hours because the yolk in their stomachs gives them all the nourishment they need during this period. If you have bought day-old-chicks which you want your broody to foster, you need to introduce them during the first night after *her* eggs have hatched, otherwise she may not accept them. Her maternal instinct is very strong and the first day is rather like a photograph – she has good colour vision and will accept various different coloured chicks but only on that first day. She cannot count but that photograph of her chicks will be imprinted on her brain and if you try and add a new chick on the third day she will not accept it and may even kill it. It is not a good idea to mix bantam and large fowl chicks due to the difference in size and the obvious risk of bullying.

Chicks should then be started on chick crumbs, which they need to eat for the first six to eight weeks. Chick crumbs also contain a coccidiostat, an anti-parasite drug that is intended to prevent intestinal disease caused by a single-celled parasite named coccidia.

If eggs under your broody still remain unhatched after 21 days you can test them by placing them in a bowl of hand hot water. Those that sink then bob about after a few seconds contain live chicks and should be put back under your hen. You can also shake the eggs and if you can detect liquid inside you will know these have not developed. Chicks do sometimes take a little longer than 21 days to hatch so be patient. I know someone who had eggs under a Silkie which hatched on the 25th day (she was sitting on wood which may have slowed the incubation process).

Mother Hen will be happy to eat the chick feed as she gradually regains her strength after days of semi-starvation. Feeding her corn is not a good idea as she will offer it to her chicks. Newly hatched chicks should be fed every couple of hours. Drinking water is also very important. In the past people used a specially designed rearing coop in which the hen stays behind bars and cannot disturb the chicks as they feed, drink and run about. This method is unnecessary, unnatural and seems dated in this modern age. It is true that a hen might become quite agitated once she is up and about, scratching the feed all over the place, upsetting the water and scattering her chicks in the process. It is therefore best not to put hay or straw in the coop once the chicks have hatched, as Mother Hen will scratch that up too and may inadvertently kick her chicks and kill or injure them. She will need to do a big poop which you should be ready to clear away.

A simple, small hen house with run attached will be ideal to accommodate hen and chicks. In any case, if they are being moved to new quarters, leave this until the evening about 24 hours after they have all hatched. Mother Hen will keep her chicks warm, teach her chicks all they need to know about life and will need a good dust bath around a few days after the chicks have hatched. The chicks will quickly learn how to dust bathe themselves at this time as well. After about five weeks the chicks will have grown enough feathers not to need to sleep under Mother Hen any more, although they may still want to. At around eight weeks Mother Hen will slowly lose her attachment to her chicks and return to the flock. She may at this time turn suddenly against the male chicks in particular, and start pecking them. Her maternal instincts disappear and her hormones are now geared for egg laying and she may start laying eggs almost straightaway. The brood of chicks however will tend to stick together once their Mum leaves. Between eight and eighteen weeks teenage chicks can be fed on growers' pellets. Be aware that you will end up with at least half of your chicks becoming cockerels.

Things that Can Go Wrong

Your mother hen may prove not to be such a good mother when her chicks hatch. I have had a tried and tested broody who having hatched her chicks was so keen to get out of her run that she trampled and killed two of them. I have also heard, on a number of occasions, of mother hens who have pecked their newly hatched chicks to death for no apparent reason. There is a possibility a mother hen is killing unhealthy or weak chicks. Chicks can sometimes be born with deformed feet and may perish as they won't be strong enough to keep up with the healthy chicks.

Hatching Eggs in an Incubator

You may wish to use an incubator to hatch your chicks. These vary in price and quality enormously and you need to follow the manufacturers' instructions very carefully. You will either have stored fertile eggs from one of your hens, or you may have bought hatching eggs. All the eggs need to be put in the incubator at the same time and they usually take slightly longer than the 21 days to hatch. The advantage of using an incubator is that you can hatch new chicks at any time of the year and you don't need to use a hen who would otherwise be laying eggs. When all the chicks have hatched you need to move them to a brooder which will have a heat lamp. They will need bedding in the form of clean white wood shavings. The heat to start with needs to be around 19 - 25°C and this can be turned down after a month. As a general rule you will need to keep the chicks under the brooder for five or six weeks. Then you can turn off the heat and keep them inside for another two weeks before transferring them outside at eight weeks, at which time you can also start feeding adult rations.

Sexing Chicks/Identifying the Cockerels

Telling the sex of day old chicks is only really possible if the feather colouring and patterning is different. In barred breeds, such as the Cuckoo Marans and barred Plymouth Rock you can tell the difference by colour as soon as the chicks hatch – the male will have a large white head spot. Males will also have wider white barring and a general lighter appearance (silvery grey) while the females will be darker. Welsummers can also be identified as chicks. The females are darker with a distinct V shape on top of their heads and black eye liner. The males will have a more smudgy V shape and not such distinct eye liner. Hybrids are sex linked so that males and females are different colours at birth. Feather sexing is used with breeds that have been specifically bred so that there is a difference in wing tip and this is done with various hybrids - females have longer wing feathers; male chicks have much shorter wings and this is noticeable within 48 hours of hatching.

With many breeds you may not realise which of your teenage chicks are cockerels until they start crowing. Your best bet is to look at the combs when your chicks are five to six weeks old. Cockerels will have definite comb development – the combs will start to redden while female chicks' combs will be smaller and paler. You may also notice that the male chicks have stumpy, curved tails and hackle feathers developing which will be longer and more pointed than the females' feathers. The pullets will have long, straight tails and their feathers on the side of the neck, flank and crop will be well advanced; their wing bows will be covered with small feathers. The wing bows of cockerels will be bare. The cockerels will also be bigger than the females at six weeks old and have thicker legs.

Disposing of the Unwanted Cockerels

Your main problem is going to be getting rid of the cockerels. You only really need one cockerel to 12 hens and since you get an average of 60% male chicks when you hatch a brood, you are almost certain to have to dispose of some of your cockerels. If you are very lucky you may be able to give them away. If you have a pure bred cockerel you may find a breeder who needs one. Otherwise they will probably have to be killed. But do make sure there are no small children around when this is done. The old fashioned way is to wring their necks but this is no job for an amateur. A trip to an obliging vet may be the best option.

The Pullets

Young female hens are called pullets right up to a year old. They may start laying eggs at around 20 to 22 weeks known as POL (Point of Lay) but everything depends on the time of the year that they hatch. If the days are shortening when they reach sexual maturity then they may not start laying until the following spring. If they have been born in February for example then they may start laying in July. Don't start pullets on layers pellets too soon. You don't want them starting to lay eggs too early in their lives as prolapse may occur (for 'prolapse' see page 101) It is advisable to start pullets on a low protein diet of wheat to avoid early maturity.

FAVOURITE EGG RECIPES

These are my favourite egg recipes that I make again and again when I have lots of eggs in the spring and summer.

SPAGHETTI ALLA CARBONARA

Serves 4

225g, 8oz spaghetti

4 eggs

2 tbsp single cream

225g, 8oz unsmoked bacon, chopped

100g, 4oz Parmesan or mature Cheddar cheese, grated

chopped parsley

Cook the spaghetti according to the packet instructions. Dry fry the bacon until crisp and beat the eggs together in a bowl with the cream. When you have drained the spaghetti add it to the bacon in the frying pan but with the pan off the heat. Quickly add the eggs and cream, stir them around and then add the grated cheese. Serve immediately, sprinkled with parsley.

EGG AND BACON QUICHE

Shortcrust pastry to line a 23cm, 9in flan dish

100g, 4oz chopped unsmoked back bacon

25g, 1oz butter

1 red onion, peeled and chopped

3 eggs

300ml, ½pt mixture of milk and single cream

75g, 3oz extra mature cheddar, grated

Prick the pastry lining the flan dish with a fork and then bake in a moderate oven for 10 minutes to half cook the pastry. Put the bacon into frying pan and dry fry for a few minutes before adding the butter and onion. Cook until the bacon is crispy and scatter over the pastry base. Whisk the eggs with the cream and milk. Pour over the bacon mixture. Spread grated cheese over the top of the tart. Cook in the oven at gas mark 4, 180°C (fan 140°C) for 25 minutes or until nicely browned on top.

VEGETARIAN EGG, CHEESE AND RED PEPPER TART

Shortcrust pastry to line a 23cm, 9in flan dish

1 tbsp olive oil

1 red pepper, deseeded and chopped into small slices

1 red onion, peeled and sliced

3 eggs

150ml, ¼pt milk

100g, 4oz cream cheese

75g, 3oz extra mature Cheddar cheese, grated

Prick the pastry lining the flan dish with a fork and then bake in a moderate oven for 10 minutes to half cook the pastry. Heat the oil in a small frying pan and fry the red pepper and onion for a few minutes until softened. Spread over the pastry base. Whisk up the eggs with the milk and cream cheese and pour over the red pepper mixture. Sprinkle grated cheese over the top and bake in the oven at gas mark 4, 180°C (fan 140°C) for 25 minutes or until nicely browned on top.

SPINACH QUICHE

Serves 4 – 6

175g, 6oz shortcrust pastry

For the filling

225g, 8oz spinach

15g, ½oz butter

300ml, ½pt single cream

4 egg yolks

100g, 4oz cream cheese

Roll out the pastry and use to line a greased 20cm, 8in flan dish. Prick the base and bake blind for 10 minutes in the oven at gas mark 4, 180°C (fan 140°C). Cook the spinach in a covered saucepan with the butter for several minutes. Chop finely and use to cover the base of the pastry case. Beat together the cream, egg yolks and cream cheese and pour over the spinach. Cook in the oven at gas mark 5, 190°C (375°F) for 30 minutes.

CREAMY EGG CURRY

Serves 4 – 6

3 tbsp olive oil

1 onion, peeled and chopped

2.5cm, 1in piece of fresh ginger, peeled and grated

1 green chilli, seeded and chopped

600ml, 1pt single cream

1 tbsp lemon juice

1 tsp of cumin seeds + 1 tsp garam masala

pinch of cayenne pepper

1 tbsp tomato purée

150ml, ¼pt vegetable stock

12 eggs, hard-boiled

3 tbsp fresh coriander, chopped

Heat the oil in a large frying pan and fry the onion for a few minutes. Add the ginger, chilli and all the other ingredients except the eggs and coriander. Bring up to a simmer. Then halve the eggs, add them to the sauce and cook for 5 minutes, stirring the sauce if it sticks to the bottom of the pan. When ready to serve transfer to a serving dish, sprinkle with the coriander and serve with boiled basmati rice and mango chutney.

CHEESE SOUFFLÉ

Serves 4

25g, 1oz butter

25g, 1oz plain flour

300ml, ½pt milk

100g, 4oz extra mature Cheddar cheese, grated

4 eggs, separated

Melt the butter in a saucepan and mix in the flour. Gradually add the milk, stirring all the time until you have a smooth roux. Remove from the heat and stir in the cheese. Then beat in the egg yolks. Whisk the egg whites and carefully fold a little into the cheese sauce. Fold in the rest, using a metal spoon. Pour into a buttered soufflé dish and bake for 30 minutes at gas mark 6, 200°C (fan 160°C) without opening the oven door. The soufflé should be golden brown on top and well risen. Serve immediately as it will collapse about 5 minutes after coming out of the oven.

SMOKED HADDOCK SOUFFLÉ

Serves 4

450g, 1lb smoked haddock

600ml, 1pt milk

50g, 2oz butter

50g, 2oz plain flour

50g, 2oz Cheddar cheese, grated

4 eggs, separated

Put the smoked haddock and milk in a saucepan and heat gently, then simmer for 5 minutes. Remove from the heat and allow the haddock to cool in the milk. Strain the milk and reserve for the sauce. Flake the fish and remove any bones and skin. Melt the butter in a saucepan and stir in the flour. Gradually add the reserved milk, stirring all the time until the sauce is smooth. Take off the heat and stir in the cheese. Stir in the yolks one at a time and stir in the flaked fish. Leave to cool while you whisk the egg whites until stiff and then fold them into the sauce. Pour into a greased soufflé dish and bake in a preheated oven at gas mark 6, 200°C (fan 160°C) for 35 minutes. Serve immediately.

SCOTCH EGGS

Serves 4

4 eggs, hard-boiled

225g, 8oz sausagemeat

1 tsp dried chopped sage

pinch of mace

1 medium onion, peeled and finely chopped

grated lemon rind from half a lemon

2 eggs, beaten

2 tbsp flour

100g, 4oz brown breadcrumbs

oil for deep frying

Fry the onions in a little butter but do not allow to brown. Mix the sausagemeat with the chopped sage, mace, onion and grated lemon rind. Divide the sausagemeat into four. Now mould each piece of sausagemeat round the egg, using your hands, until you have completely enclosed it. Next, dip each Scotch egg in some of the flour, then in the egg, repeat and then roll in the breadcrumbs. Deep fry the Scotch eggs until well browned on all sides. Halve each one and eat hot or cold.

POACHED EGGS WITH PEPPERS AND CHORIZO

This is a quick supper for two. You could serve it with potato wedges or some new potatoes.

2 eggs, softly poached

2 tbsp olive oil

1 red and 1 yellow pepper, deseeded and sliced

100g, 4oz Chorizo, sliced

50g, 2oz rocket leaves

Heat the oil in a pan and fry the pepper slices, add the chorizo and warm through. Arrange the mixture on a small serving dish and top with the poached eggs. Sprinkle over the rocket and serve with a vinaigrette dressing.

CHEESY EGG, BACON AND RICE DISH

Serves 4 – 6

2 tbsp olive oil

1 onion, peeled and chopped

150g, 5oz back bacon

225g, 8oz long grain brown rice

600ml, 1pt vegetable stock

3 eggs, hard-boiled

15g, ½oz butter

1 tbsp flour

150ml, ¼pt milk

75g, 3oz mature Cheddar cheese

2 tbsp brown breadcrumbs

pinch of cayenne pepper (optional)

Heat the oil in a casserole and soften the onion. Chop the bacon and add to the onion. Fry for 5 minutes, then add the rice and stir to coat it in the oil. Add the stock, cover and simmer for 40 minutes. Slice the eggs and spread over the top of the rice. Make the sauce by melting the butter, stirring in the flour and gradually adding the milk. Stir until smooth and pour over the eggs. Sprinkle the cheese, breadcrumbs and cayenne pepper over the sauce and put under a hot grill for a couple of minutes to brown the top. Serve at once with garlic bread and a salad.

SALADE NICOISE

There are many versions of this classic French salad.

Serves 6

Handful of salad leaves

150g, 5oz French beans

½ cucumber, cut into sticks

1 red onion, peeled and sliced thinly

6 eggs, hard-boiled

200g, 7oz tin of tuna steaks in oil, drained

handful of cherry tomatoes, halved

50g, 2oz tin of anchovies

50g, 2oz black olives

Dressing

5 tbsp olIve oil + 1 tbsp balsamic vinegar

1 clove of garlic, peeled and crushed + salt and pepper

First cook the French beans in boiling water for 3 or 4 minutes, drain and put under cold running water to retain their green colour. Arrange the salad leaves in a bowl and spread the beans, onion and cucumber over them. Halve the boiled eggs and add to the salad along with the tuna, tomatoes, anchovies and olives. For the dressing stir together the oil, vinegar, garlic and salt and pepper and pour over the salad.

MAYONNAISE

2 egg yolks

1 tsp mustard powder

1 tsp sugar

salt and black pepper

150ml, ¼pt olive oil

150ml, ¼pt sunflower oil

3 tbsp white wine vinegar

Put the egg yolks, mustard powder, sugar and seasoning in a food processor and whiz for a few seconds. Start adding the oil, drip by drip and then in a slow steady trickle. Do not add it too fast or the mixture will curdle. When you have added about half of the oils you can add the vinegar tablespoon by tablespoon. Then add the rest of the oil in the same way as before. If the mixture curdles you can rescue it by adding another egg yolk. Beat the extra yolk and then add the curdled mayonnaise to it very slowly, beating all the time. This should give you a smooth mayonnaise.

HOLLANDAISE SAUCE

2 egg yolks

1 tsp white wine vinegar

75g, 3oz hot melted butter

Whiz the egg yolks in a blender or small food processor with the teaspoon of white wine vinegar. Pour the melted butter gradually onto the egg yolks with the motor still running. The sauce will thicken. Serve immediately.

VANILLA CUSTARD

2 egg yolks

1 tbsp sugar

300ml, ½pt full fat milk

1 tsp vanilla essence or ½ vanilla pod, split

Whisk the egg yolks. Put the sugar, milk and essence or vanilla pod together in a saucepan and bring slowly to the boil. Remove the pod if using and pour the milk onto the egg yolks. Return to the pan and stir over a gentle heat until the liquid thickens. Serve hot or cold.

WHITE CHOCOLATE HEAVENS

Serves 5

These are little white chocolate ice creams frozen in ramekins.

75g, 3oz white chocolate +1 tbsp single cream

3 egg yolks

50g, 2oz caster sugar

210ml, 7fl oz double cream

Melt the white chocolate in the microwave or over a pan of simmering water. Stir in the single cream – this will help give a smooth texture. Whisk the egg yolks and sugar together until thick and creamy. Then fold in the melted white chocolate, followed by the double cream. Pour into 5 ramekin dishes and freeze.

MASCARPONE ICE CREAM

Serves 6

2 egg yolks

50g, 2oz icing sugar

225g, 8oz mascarpone

2 tsp vanilla essence

Whisk together the egg yolks and icing sugar until really thick. Beat the mascarpone and vanilla essence into the egg yolk mixture. Transfer to a freezer container and freeze until firm.

TREACLE TART ICE CREAM

Serves 6 - 8

50g, 2oz brown breadcrumbs

40g, 1½oz melted butter

6 egg yolks

150ml, ¼pt golden syrup, warmed

1 tbsp lemon juice

300ml, ½pt whipping cream, whipped

Mix together the breadcrumbs and melted butter. Put under the grill for a few minutes laid out on a baking sheet to crisp. Whisk the egg yolks until thick and pour the golden syrup in a steady stream onto the yolks as you whisk them. Whisk in the lemon juice. Stir in the whipped cream and fold in the cooled breadcrumbs. Turn into a freezer container and freeze until firm.

WHITE CHOCOLATE ICE CREAM

This ice cream is really quick to make and a great way to use up surplus eggs.

4 eggs, separated

100g, 4oz icing sugar

1 tsp vanilla essence

300ml, ½pt double cream

100g, 4oz white chocolate, chopped

Put the yolks in one bowl and the egg whites in another. Whisk the egg whites first and when foamy gradually add half the icing sugar, a spoon at a time. Whisk until thick. Use the same whisk to whip up the yolks with the rest of the icing sugar and the vanilla essence. Keep whisking until thick. Whip the cream. Stir the egg yolk mixture into the cream and lastly fold in the egg white. Freeze until soft. Fold in the white chocolate until evenly distributed.

CARAMEL ICE CREAM

Serves 6

175g, 6oz granulated sugar

3 tbsp water

3 tbsp evaporated milk

3 egg yolks

250ml, 8fl oz double cream, whipped

Dissolve the sugar in a small saucepan with the water. Bring to the boil and boil until a rich golden colour. Turn off the heat and mix in the evaporated milk, standing back as the mixture will froth up. Stir until smooth. Whisk the egg yolks until thick and mix in the caramel plus any fudgy bits that have accumulated. Leave to cool and then fold in the cream. Pour into a freezer container and freeze.

LEMON CURD ICE CREAM

Serves 6 – 8

4 eggs, separated

225g, 8oz lemon curd

300ml, ½pt whipping cream, whipped

50g, 2oz icing sugar

Whisk the egg yolks into the lemon curd. Fold into the whipped cream. Whisk the egg whites and whisk in the icing sugar. Fold into the lemon cream until evenly blended. Put into a freezer container and freeze.

LEMON CURD

Makes 450g, 1lb

2 eggs

150g, 5oz caster sugar

50g, 2oz butter

grated rind and juice of 2 lemons

In a mixing bowl beat the eggs and add the sugar, butter, lemon rind and juice. Put this bowl over a pan of simmering water and stir the mixture from time to time until it thickens. Leave to cool and pour into jars.

LEMON FUDGE TART

Serves 6 – 8

Sweet shortcrust pastry to fit a 23cm, 9in flan dish

5 eggs

grated rind and juice of 4 lemons

275g, 10oz caster sugar

150g, 5oz butter

Roll out the pastry and use to line the flan dish. Prick and bake blind in the oven for 15 minutes at gas mark 4, 180°C (fan 140°C). Meanwhile melt the butter. Whisk the eggs, sugar, lemon juice and grated rind and whisk in the melted butter. Pour over the pastry base while it is still warm. Return to the oven and cook for another 25 minutes. Serve warm.

MERINGUES

4 egg whites

100g, 4oz Demerara sugar

100g, 4oz granulated sugar

Whisk the egg whites until stiff. Mix together the two sugars and while you continue to whisk the egg whites, whisk in a tablespoon of sugar at a time until all is incorporated. The meringue should be very stiff. Put spoonfuls onto greased baking sheets and warm the oven. Cook the meringues for 20 minutes at gas mark 1, 130°C (fan 100°C) and then reduce to gas mark ½ 120°C (fan 80°C) and cook for another 2 hours. Leave in the oven until completely cold.

WHITE CHOCOLATE MOUSSE

Serves 6 – 8

275g, 10oz white chocolate

50g, 2oz unsalted butter

4 tbsp single cream

5 eggs, separated

1 tsp vanilla essence

150ml, ¼pt double cream, whipped

Melt the chocolate with the butter and cream in the microwave. Stir together until smooth. Beat in the egg yolks with the vanilla essence and leave to cool a little. Fold in the cream. Whisk the egg whites until firm and fold into the white chocolate mixture. Pour into a serving bowl and leave to set in the fridge. No gelatine is needed!

CRÈME CARAMELS

Makes 8 ramekins

175g, 6oz granulated sugar

150ml, ¼pt water

3 eggs plus 2 egg yolks

300ml, milk or half milk and half single cream

50g, 2oz caster sugar

1tsp vanilla extract

Combine the water and granulated sugar in a saucepan and heat gently until the sugar has dissolved. Bring to the boil and cook without stirring until the mixture is golden brown. Pour into eight individual ramekin dishes. Beat the egg yolks, whole eggs, caster sugar and vanilla extract together. Warm the milk and stir into the egg mixture. Strain and pour on to the caramelised sugar. Fill a roasting tin half full with water and place the ramekin dishes in the tin; cover with silver foil. Bake in the oven at gas mark 3, 160°C (fan 120°C) for 50 minutes or until set. Cool and then chill for at least 24 hours before serving. If you turn out the puddings too soon, the caramelised sugar will still be hard at the bottom of the ramekins. You don't want to miss out on that lovely caramel sauce.

CARAMEL CUSTARD POTS

These use similar ingredients to crème caramels but are easier to make and even more delicious. The burnt caramel which is the sauce in crème caramels gets incorporated into the main mixture.

75g, 3oz granulated sugar

160ml, 5fl oz milk combined with 160ml, 5fl oz double cream or with evaporated milk

4 egg yolks

50g, 2oz caster sugar

¼ tsp salt

½ tsp vanilla essence

Heat the sugar in a heavy based saucepan. The sugar will turn to liquid and go brown. As soon as this happens, turn off the heat and start pouring the milk and cream onto the sugar. The sugar will bubble up and turn hard. Just keep stirring the liquid in. Turn the heat back on and gradually the sugar will melt into the cream. If you get a few hard bits of sugar left in the milk, so much the better. Allow to cool a little while you lightly beat the egg yolks with the sugar, salt and vanilla essence. Beat in the creamy liquid including any hard bits of sugar. Transfer to a jug in order to pour equal amounts of the custard into 5 ramekins. Distribute any hard bits of sugar between the ramekins. Cover with foil. Bake in the oven at gas mark 3,

160°C (fan 120°C) for about 40 minutes or until just wobbly in the centre. Allow to cool and then put in the fridge for a couple of hours. The mixture will become more solid as it cools. Any hard bits of sugar will have developed into a delicious caramel sauce revealed under the custard.

MERINGUE BISCUITS

These are light crispy biscuits. You can sandwich them together with butter cream.

2 egg whites

100g, 4oz soft brown sugar

75g, 3oz crushed walnuts or pecans

Beat the egg whites until stiff and then continue whisking while you add the brown sugar, a tablespoon at a time. When all the sugar is incorporated you should have a thick meringue mixture which stands in peaks. Fold in the crushed nuts. Grease a couple of Swiss roll tins and pop spoonfuls of the mixture well separated on the tin. Spread each biscuit mixture out with a spatula so that it is about the thickness of a pound coin. Bake in the oven at gas mark 3, 160°C (fan 120°C) for about 8 minutes. You want the biscuits to have browned and become crispy. If they are undercooked they will be more chewy. They will be quite fragile; allow to cool and then lift from the baking tin and eat as they are or sandwich with a vanilla flavoured butter cream.

CRÈME BRULEE

Serves 6

4 egg yolks

50g, 2oz caster sugar

1 tsp vanilla essence

600ml, 1pt single cream

50g, 2oz demerara sugar

Beat the egg yolks with the sugar and beat in the vanilla essence. Heat the cream over a pan of simmering water until just below boiling point. Stir into the egg yolk mixture and strain into 6 greased ramekin dishes. Place the ramekins into a roasting tin half filled with water and bake in the oven at gas mark 4, 180°C (fan 140°C) for about 25 minutes until just set. Leave to cool. Sprinkle demerara sugar over the top of each ramekin and put under the grill to caramelise or use a blow torch. Chill for about two hours before serving. Don't chill for too long or the caramel topping will go soft.

LIGHT LEMON SPONGE

100g, 4oz caster sugar

3 eggs, separated

1 tbsp lemon juice

50g, 2oz plain flour + ½ tsp baking powder

25g, 1oz cornflour

Filling

50g, 2oz butter

100g, 4oz icing sugar

¼ tsp grated lemon zest + 1 tsp lemon juice

Icing

100g, 4 oz icing sugar+ 2 tbsp lemon juice

Beat together the egg yolks and sugar until light and creamy. Stir in the lemon juice. Sift the flour, cornflour and baking powder and fold carefully into the egg and sugar mixture. Beat the egg whites until fairly stiff and fold them in as well. Divide the mixture between two 17.5cm, 7in greased cake tins, lined with baking parchment. Bake in the oven at gas mark 4, 180°C (fan 140°C) for 15 minutes. Remove and allow to cool on a wire rack. To make the filling beat the butter and gradually beat in the icing sugar. Add the lemon zest and juice and beat again. Use this butter cream to sandwich the two cakes together. Mix the lemon juice with the icing sugar and pour this over the cake. Leave to set. This cake is best eaten the day it is made or at least by the next day.

SWISS ROLL

3 eggs

75g, 3oz caster sugar

1 tsp vanilla extract

40g, 1½oz plain flour

40g 1½oz cornflour

4 – 5 tbsp of Blackberry jelly

150ml, ¼pt double cream, whipped

Whisk the eggs and sugar together until the mixture is thick and leaves a trail when you lift some of the mixture up. Sieve the flour and cornflour over the egg and gently fold in with a metal spoon. Spread the mixture onto a Swiss roll tin lined with greaseproof paper. Bake in the oven at gas mark 4, 180°C (fan 140°C) for 10 minutes. Remove from the oven and tip onto a clean tea towel. Spread jam evenly over the surface. Allow to cool before spreading the cream on top of the jelly.

ANGEL FOOD CAKE

This is a white cake using just the egg white – it is a bit like a meringue mixture but with the flour added becomes spongy. This is good as a teatime treat with a fudge icing. Alternatively you could serve with summer fruits and cream.

3 egg whites

½ tsp cream of tartar

½ tsp vanilla extract

100g, 4oz caster sugar

60g, 2½oz plain flour

Fudge icing

25g, 1oz butter

50g, 2oz brown sugar

2 tbsp single cream

100g, 4oz icing sugar

Whisk the egg whites until frothy, then add the cream of tartar and whisk until stiff. Sift the sugar and flours together and lightly fold into the egg white. Add the vanilla essence as well. Turn into a greased 20cm, 8in cake tin and bake in the oven at gas mark 3, 160°C (fan 120°C) for 30 minutes. To make the icing melt the butter and brown sugar in a saucepan. Bring to the boil then add the cream and simmer for a few minutes. Take off the heat and beat in the icing sugar. Top the cake with fudge icing.

PRESERVING EGGS

If you are separating your eggs and wish to use only the whites, you can store the yolks in the fridge for up to two days covered with a little water to prevent a skin forming. Alternatively, if you are using the yolks, you can store the whites in the fridge for up to a week but in this case it is best to use them in cooked dishes.

Freezing Eggs If in the spring you find yourself inundated with eggs, you can freeze them. Raw eggs must be frozen out of their shells and you can either freeze the yolks and whites separately or together. Separate the yolks from the whites – it is important that for this method the eggs are very fresh as stale yolks are liable to break and you don't want yolk in the egg white. Add either a little salt or a little sugar to the yolks and freeze in a suitable container. Whites can be frozen as they are, but cooked whites do not freeze well. Cooked yolks are okay frozen if incorporated into another dish. Whole raw eggs frozen in small containers can be fried or poached straight from the freezer.

Storage in Waterglass Storing eggs in waterglass is an old method of preserving eggs which may be of interest. You can store eggs for up to a year by putting them in waterglass solution (soluble sodium silicate). This seals the pores in the shell preventing the loss of moisture from the inside and keeps out bacteria. In other words, by storing eggs in waterglass you are making their shells impervious. You should only use fresh, unwashed, uncracked eggs. Sodium silicate can be bought as a concentrated solution in a tin in the chemist. It may be difficult to find as the demand is not great nowadays but try old fashioned chemists or ironmongers – a 300ml, ½pt tin of sodium silicate will be enough to preserve 80 eggs. You should mix the sodium silicate powder with an equal part in weight of water and then this solution is diluted by one part to 20 parts of water. Earthenware jars or enamel buckets are the best containers to use. Fill with the solution and place the eggs carefully in the container, broad end uppermost with about 5cm, 2in of solution above the eggs. You should cover the container and since water will evaporate you will need occasionally to top up the solution. When you want to use any eggs, wash them thoroughly under running cold water and prick them with a pin if you want to boil them.

Pickling Eggs

You could try pickling surplus eggs. First you need to hard-boil them. For about 14 hard-boiled eggs you need 900ml, 1½pt of white wine vinegar. Simmer the vinegar with a small piece of root ginger and a tablespoon of white peppercorns for about 15 minutes. Allow to cool and strain. Peel the eggs and arrange in a large glass jar. Add one red chilli pepper and then pour on the spiced vinegar. Seal and leave for a couple of weeks before using.

GLOSSARY

Air Space, sac or cell The air space at the broad end of the egg which expands with age or in a fertile egg provides the chick with air before hatching.

Autosexing Method by which chicks can be sexed when they hatch by the colour of their down.

Barring Alternative strips of two distinct colours across the feathers.

Blastoderm The germ in a fertile egg identified as a spot in the yolk.

Blood Spots The spots of blood formed on the yolk of an egg which are caused by the rupture of small blood vessels during the formation of the egg.

Candling Examining an egg under bright light in order to look at its interior, usually to see if it is fertilised.

Chalazae Stringy bands of protein which hold the yolk in place inside the white.

China or Crock Eggs 'Pretend' eggs used to encourage hens to lay in a particular nest or to test for broodiness.

Columbian The basic colour is white but there is black lacing in the neck and tail feathers are black. There is also a buff Columbian colour variation where the basic colour is light brown with black lacing in the neck and black tail feathers.

Cuckoo Cuckoo Barring is a term for colouring where two colours running across the feathers are not distinctive and merge into each other. A good example is the Cuckoo Marans.

Down The covering of hair on baby chicks sometimes referred to as fluff.

Dual Purpose A breed that is good for meat as well as eggs.

Egg Tooth The hard horny tip on a newly hatched chick's beak used for chipping its way out of the shell. It falls off later.

Feathered Legs Feathers cover the legs of the bird as in breeds such as Brahma, Cochin, Pekin and Faverolles.

Frizzled A term used for curled feathers as in the Frizzle Breed.

In-Breeding The mating of closely related birds, not be recommended.

Lacing Feather marking in which edging is of a different colour to the inside of the feather.

Millefleur A colour combination of black, white and brown feathers. The black feathers are tipped with white. Lemon millefleur gives a yellow coloured feathers tipped with black.

Mottling Feather marking where there are spots of a different colour at the end of the feather.

Muffled An abundance of feathers on each side of the face.

Non sitters Non-sitters are breeds which do not go broody and tend therefore to lay more eggs and include Ancona, Welsummer, Leghorn, Minorca, Hamburgh and Poland.

Oviduct Long tube where egg formation takes place which leads from the ovary to the cloaca.

Partridge This is a combination of colour and markings on the bird's plumage. The colour partridge varies in different breeds. Partridge Wyandotte hens are brown with black pencilling while Partridge Welsummer hens are bay with greyish, black peppering and a salmon breast; Partridge cockerels are a combination of black, red and brown. Colour variations though make it complicated – the brown feather parts can be bred in different colours so there are blue, white, yellow and cuckoo partridge varieties as with the Dutch bantams.

Pea Comb A triple comb as if three single combs have been joined together.

Pencilling Small markings of stripes across the feather as in the Hamburgh or concentric in form following the outline of the feather as in the silver pencilled Wyandotte

Porcelaine A grey and lemon coloured overall effect.

Pullet A young female bird of 12 months or less.

Pyle This is a colour. Hens are a combination of salmon breast, gold coloured necks with cream over the rest of their bodies. Cockerels are red with some brown and white.

Quail This is used to denote a colour. Quail is typical of Belgian breeds and is similar to partridge; the hen has a golden brown breast with a combination of black and gold on the rest of her body. The cockerel is also a mixture of gold and black.

Rose Comb A broad flat comb covered with small points.

Sitters Breeds such as Orpington, Plymouth Rock, Rhode Island Red, Marans, Wyandotte, Sussex and Dorking are all sitters which means they go broody and sit easily.

Splash An overall light grey colour with blotches of darker grey.

Spangling Large spots of colour on the feathers different from the ground colour.

Tinted This refers to the colour of cream or very light brown eggs.

Triple Comb See Pea Comb

Wheaten The colour is a combination of browns – golden wheat and light brown with cream-coloured breast. Wheaten Marans has black flecks in the neck feathers.

Index

M

N

O

P

Q

R